SAUNDERS MATHEMATICS BOOKS

Consulting Editor

BERNARD R. GELBAUM, *University of California*

Lectures on

REAL AND
COMPLEX
VECTOR SPACES

FRANK S. CATER

Assistant Professor of Mathematics
Portland State College, Portland, Oregon

W. B. SAUNDERS COMPANY
Philadelphia and London, 1966

W. B. Saunders Company: West Washington Square
Philadelphia, Pa. 19105

12 Dyott Street
London W.C.1

Lectures on Real and Complex Vector Spaces

Preface

Parts 1, 2, and 3 and Lectures 5-1, 5-2, and 5-3 in this text can be studied in an undergraduate course on vector spaces. First year graduate students and mathematically mature seniors should also be able to digest all of Parts 4 and 5. In recent years many textbooks have been published for undergraduate courses in vector spaces and linear algebra. I have endeavored to include more nontrivial material in this text than is ordinarily found in these works. I hope that Parts 4 and 5 and part of Part 3 can be read without boredom by the expert as well as the student. All the theorems presented in the text are more or less known; one or two of the proofs are possibly new.

Most of the work in Part 4 is ordinarily developed by means of modules, rings, and ideals in rings. All results are proved by employing elementary vector space techniques. In Lectures 5-5 and 5-6 there is given some of the elementary material concerning von Neumann algebras on finite dimensional Hilbert spaces. The discussion is given for the finite dimensional case and thereby most of the complications concerning continuity and convergence are avoided; however, the arguments that remain should give the nonexpert the essence of the more general proofs. In Part 5 there is given a treatment of partial isometries and the uniqueness of the polar decomposition of an operator, topics often neglected in a text of this nature. In Part 3 the classic results concerning the characteristic polynomial and the Jordan Form of an operator are detailed. The characteristic polynomial and its properties (including the Cayley-Hamilton equation) are treated without employing determinants. The uniqueness of the Jordan Form of an operator is proved by considering the dimensions of the range spaces of certain nilpotent operators. Most of the lectures are followed by a list of problems. Though many of these are routine problems one can find in several books, there are a few which would be hard to locate elsewhere.

I have purposely limited the field of scalars to the real and complex fields in order to avoid a discussion of fields, characteristics of fields, and other properties of fields. However, the algebraist will recognize that most of our proofs on complex vector spaces are valid for vector spaces over an algebraically closed field. Likewise, proofs concerning real and complex vector spaces are usually valid for any vector space over a field (not of characteristic 2).

For readers primarily interested in rings and modules, a more abstract development of most of our work in Part 4 can be found in (or pieced together from) the books "Infinite Abelian Groups" by I. Kaplansky [9], "Abstract Algebra," vol. II, and "Structure of Rings" by N. Jacobson [7, 8], and the linear algebra book of Bourbaki. For those persons primarily interested in Hilbert space operators and von Neumann algebras Chapter VII of "Real Analysis" by Botts and McShane [2], "Introduction to Hilbert Space" by S. K. Berberian [1], and "Les Algèbres d'Opérateurs dans l'Espace Hilbertien" by J. Dixmier [4] will serve. For those readers interested in vector spaces over fields other than the real or complex field "Finite Dimensional Vector Spaces" by P. R. Halmos [6] will be useful. For a more lengthy presentation of elementary topics "Linear Algebra" by Charles W. Curtis [3] is suggested.

To read Parts 1, 2, and 3 one should be familiar with the elementary properties of real and complex numbers and naive set theory. Some mathematical maturity is also required. Parts 4 and 5 demand an even higher level of maturity. The text is otherwise self-contained and begins with elementary concepts.

The following gives a summary of the organization of the book. The text is divided into five parts, and each part consists of several lectures. The lectures are identified in the following way: the n-th lecture of Part m is denoted Lecture m-n. Thus Lecture 2-3 is the third lecture of Part 2, and Lecture 5-4 is the fourth lecture of Part 5. Many of the problems left to the reader fill gaps in the text. The purpose of these problems is twofold; first, to encourage the reader to prove the simpler steps in the development for himself, and second, to prevent the text from being inundated by trivial arguments. As the reader progresses through the text he is asked to supply more and more of the details. Compare Part 1, for example, with Parts 4 and 5.

I am indebted to Professor Charles W. Curtis and Professor Donald K. Harrison of the University of Oregon for discussions of some of the more difficult points. Though I have not listed all my sources, I am also indebted to the authors of the books on vector spaces and linear algebra I have studied.

Portland, Oregon   F. S. C.

Contents

Lecture 5–6

Part 1   FUNDAMENTAL
CONCEPTS

Lecture 1–1

Introduction. In this lecture we outline briefly what we expect the reader to know about naive set theory and logical proof. It is not our intention to present a discourse on these topics, so we refer the reader to "Naive Set Theory" by P. R. Halmos [5] and the appendix of "Algebra of Matrices" by Malcolm F. Smiley [12].

If x is an element and A is a set, the expression $x \in A$ means that x is an element in A, and the expression $x \notin A$ means that x is not an element in A. If A and B are sets, then $A \cup B$ denotes the set of all elements in A or B or both, $A \cap B$ denotes the set of all elements both in A and B, and $A - B$ denotes the set of all elements in A but not in B. The expression $A \subset B$ means that every element in A is also in B. The symbol $\varnothing$ often denotes the void set. If $\{E_\alpha\}$ is a family of sets, the sets $\bigcup_\alpha E_\alpha$ and $\bigcap_\alpha E_\alpha$ are the sets of all elements x respectively in some or all E_α.

Let R be a binary relation between pairs of elements of a set A. We say that R is *reflexive* if xRx for each $x \in A$; R is *symmetric* if xRy implies yRx for any $x, y \in A$; and R is *transitive* if xRy and yRz imply xRz for any $x, y, z \in A$. If R is reflexive, symmetric, and transitive, we say that R is an *equivalence relation*. If R is an equivalence relation, then A can be partitioned into pairwise disjoint subsets such that xRy holds iff x and y are in the same subset. (The word "iff" will henceforth denote "if and only if.")

By a *mapping* (or *function*) of a set A into a set B we mean a rule assigning to each element of A a unique element of B. An equivalent definition reads as follows; a mapping of A into B is a family of ordered pairs $\mathscr{S} = \{(x, y)\}$, $x \in A$, $y \in B$, such that for each $x \in A$ there is exactly one $y \in B$ satisfying $(x, y) \in \mathscr{S}$. We say that f is 1–1 if $x_1 \neq x_2$ implies $f(x_1) \neq f(x_2)$. We say that f maps A onto B if $f(A) = B$. A 1–1 mapping of A onto B is sometimes called a 1–1 correspondence between A and B.

We say that a set E is finite if it is void or can be put into 1–1 correspondence with the set of integers $\{1, 2, \ldots, n\}$ for some n. Otherwise E is infinite. If E is infinite, then E can be put into 1–1 correspondence with a proper subset of itself. We say that E is countable if it is finite or if it can be put into 1–1 correspondence with the positive integers. Otherwise E is uncountable.

3

We expect the reader to be familiar with proof by mathematical induction. The principle can be stated as follows. Let $P(n)$ be a statement about a positive integer n ($P(n)$ may or may not be true). If $P(k)$ implies $P(k + 1)$ for any positive integer k and if $P(1)$ is true, then $P(n)$ must be true for each positive integer n.

We also expect the reader to be familiar with indirect proof (proof by contradiction) and other types of logical arguments frequently employed in mathematics.

Now let $\{E_\alpha\}$ be a family of subsets of a set X. We say that a subfamily $\{S_\beta\}$ of $\{E_\alpha\}$ is a *nest* if whenever A and B lie in $\{S_\beta\}$ either $A \subset B$ or $B \subset A$. In Part 4 we shall assume the

Maximum Principle.   *Let $\{E_\alpha\}$ be a nonvoid family of subsets of a set X such that for each nest $\{S_\beta\}$ in $\{E_\alpha\}$, there exists a set in $\{E_\alpha\}$ of which all members of $\{S_\beta\}$ are subsets. Then there is a maximal set E_{α_0} in $\{E_\alpha\}$; i.e., if E_α is any set satisfying $E_{\alpha_0} \subset E_\alpha$, then $E_\alpha = E_{\alpha_0}$.*

The Maximum Principle is obviously valid if X is a finite set, and it seems plausible when X is infinite. It can be shown (see "General Topology" by J. L. Kelley [10], pp. 31–36, 273–274) that the Maximum Principle is logically equivalent to the

Choice Axiom.   *Let A be a set of indices, and for each $\alpha \in A$ let E_α be a nonvoid set. Then there exists a mapping f of A into $\bigcup_{\alpha \in A} E_\alpha$ such that $f(\alpha) \in E_\alpha$ for each $\alpha \in A$.*

In other words, we can choose simultaneously an element in every E_α. The Choice Axiom will also be employed in Part 4.

Problems for Lecture 1—1

1. Let f and g be mappings of a set A into A such that the composition fg is the identity mapping on A. Prove that g is 1–1 and that f maps A onto A. Must f be 1–1? Explain.

2. Let A be the set of all living people. Let xRy mean that x and y have the same mother. Is R an equivalence relation? Let $xR'y$ mean that x knows y. Is R' an equivalence relation?

3. Let A denote the set of all husbands and B denote the set of all wives (we will assume that society practices monogamy). Construct a 1–1 mapping of A onto B. Does there exist a 1–1 mapping of A onto a proper subset of B? Explain.

4. Let A, B, and C be sets. Prove $(C - A) \cup (C - B) = C - (A \cap B)$ and $(C - A) \cap (C - B) = C - (A \cup B)$, where, generally, $X - Y$ is the set of elements in X but not in Y.

5. Let A, B, and C be sets. Prove $A \cap (B \cup C) = (A \cap B) \cup (A \cap C)$ and $A \cup (B \cap C) = (A \cup B) \cap (A \cup C)$.

6. Let X be a countably infinite set. Prove there exists an uncountable family M of subsets of X satisfying
  (a) the intersection of no two members of M is infinite,
  (b) for each countably infinite subfamily N of M there exists an $A \in M - N$ such that $(\bigcup_{B \in N} B) \cap A$ is infinite.
  (Hint: this requires Zorn's axiom.)

Lecture 1–2

Real and Complex Numbers and Polynomials. Throughout our book we shall assume that the reader is familiar with the real numbers, complex numbers, and the operations of addition and multiplication of numbers. The following properties are true of both the real and complex numbers.

(1) $a + b = b + a$ and $ab = ba$ for any numbers a and b.

(2) $a + (b + c) = (a + b) + c$ and $a(bc) = (ab)c$ for any numbers a, b, and c.

(3) $a(b + c) = ab + ac$ for any numbers a, b, and c.

(4) There exists a number 0 such that $a + 0 = a$ for any number a.

(5) For each number a there exists a number $-a$ such that $a + (-a) = 0$.

(6) There exists a number 1 different from 0 such that $a1 = a$ for any number a.

(7) For each nonzero number a there exists a number a^{-1} such that $aa^{-1} = 1$.

From these properties we can also derive the following conclusions. For any number a we have $a0 = a(0 + 0) = a0 + a0$ and $a0 = 0$. For any numbers a and b we have $[a + (-a)]b = 0b = 0 = ab + (-a)b$ and $(-a)b = -(ab)$. Likewise $(-a)(-b) = ab$, and in particular, $(-1)(-1) = 1$. We let $a - b$ denote $a + (-b)$.

Furthermore, the nonzero real numbers are partitioned into two nonvoid disjoint classes, the positive numbers and the negative numbers, such that the sum of any two positive numbers is positive and the product of any two positive numbers is positive. For any real number $a \neq 0$, either a or $-a$ is positive. It can be shown that a is positive iff $-a$ is negative, and a is negative iff $-a$ is positive. We say that $a < b$ if $b - a$ is positive. For real numbers a and b, either $a < b$, $b < a$, or $a = b$, and no two of these statements hold simultaneously. This defines an ordering of the real numbers.

In Part 5 we shall have occasion to employ some more advanced properties of the real and complex numbers. For these we refer to the development of the real numbers given in "Principles of Mathematical Analysis" by Walter Rudin [11].

By a *polynomial* we mean a sequence $(a_0, a_1, a_2, \ldots)$ of complex numbers such that all but finitely many numbers in the sequence are 0. (Note that the first entry of the sequence is given the index 0, the second entry 1, the third entry 2, and so on.) By the *degree* of the polynomial we mean the nonnegative integer k such that $a_k \neq 0$ and $0 = a_{k+1} = a_{k+2} = \cdots$. For example, the degree is 0 if $0 = a_1 = a_2 = \cdots$ and $a_0 \neq 0$. We say that the polynomial $(0, 0, 0, \ldots)$ has no degree. By a *monic* polynomial we mean a polynomial of degree k where $a_k = 1$. By a polynomial *without constant term* we mean a polynomial with $a_0 = 0$.

Let $p = (a_0, a_1, \ldots)$ and $q = (b_0, b_1, \ldots)$ be polynomials. We define the sum $p + q$ of these polynomials to be $(a_0 + b_0, a_1 + b_1, \ldots)$. Clearly degree $(p + q)$ cannot exceed both degree p and degree q. We define the product pq to be the polynomial $(c_0, c_1, \ldots)$ where $c_j = \sum_{i=0}^{j} a_i b_{j-i}$ for each index $j = 0, 1, \ldots$. If $h =$ degree p, $k =$ degree q, then $c_{h+k} = \sum_{i=0}^{h+k} a_i b_{h+k-i} = a_h b_k \neq 0$, and $0 = c_{h+k+1} = c_{h+k+2} = \cdots$. Hence degree $(pq) =$ degree $p +$ degree q. We claim that the polynomials under these rules of addition and multiplication enjoy properties (1) to (6) just given. (Two polynomials are said to be equal if they are identical; to wit, the sequences have the same entries.) Property (1) follows from the equations $a_j + b_j = b_j + a_j$ and $\sum_{i=0}^{j} a_i b_{j-i} = \sum_{i=0}^{j} b_i a_{j-i}$. Property (2) follows from the equations $a_j + (b_j + c_j) = (a_j + b_j) + c_j$ and

$$\sum_{i=0}^{j} a_i \left(\sum_{k=0}^{j-i} b_k c_{j-i-k} \right) = \sum_{i+h+k=j} a_i b_h c_k = \sum_{i=0}^{i} \left(\sum_{k=0}^{i} a_k b_{i-k} \right) c_{j-i}$$

for each j. Property (3) follows from the equation

$$\sum_{i=0}^{j} a_i (b_{j-i} + c_{j-i}) = \sum_{i=0}^{j} a_i b_{j-i} + \sum_{i=0}^{j} a_i c_{j-i}.$$

For the zero polynomial we take $(0, 0, \ldots)$. Clearly $(0, 0, \ldots) + (a_0, a_1, \ldots) = (a_0, a_1, \ldots)$ and this establishes (4). For the polynomial $p = (a_0, a_1, \ldots)$ we take $-p$ to be $(-a_0, -a_1, \ldots)$. Clearly $p + (-p) = 0$ (where 0 here denotes the zero polynomial). For the identity polynomial we take $(1, 0, 0, \ldots)$. Then $(1, 0, 0, \ldots)(a_0, a_1, a_2, \ldots) = (a_0, a_1, a_2, \ldots)$. Hence (6) is established.

However (7) is not satisfied by the polynomials. There cannot exist a polynomial p such that $(0, 1, 0, \ldots)p = (1, 0, 0, \ldots)$ because the degree of the left side cannot be 0.

Note that $(a_0, 0, 0, \ldots)(b_0, 0, 0, \ldots) = (a_0 b_0, 0, 0, \ldots)$ and $(a_0, 0, 0, \ldots) + (b_0, 0, 0, \ldots) = (a_0 + b_0, 0, 0, \ldots)$. Making a slight abuse of language we call the polynomial $(a_0, 0, 0, \ldots)$, a_0. Let x denote the polynomial $(0, 1, 0, 0, \ldots)$. It follows (Problem 1) that $(a_0, a_1, a_2, \ldots) = a_0 + a_1 x + a_2 x^2 + \cdots$. The rules for addition and multiplication of polynomials given before now read as follows;

$$(a_0 + a_1 x + a_2 x^2 + \cdots) + (b_0 + b_1 x + b_2 x^2 + \cdots)$$
$$= (a_0 + b_0) + (a_1 + b_1)x + (a_2 + b_2)x^2 + \cdots$$

and

$$(a_0 + a_1x + a_2x^2 + \cdots)(b_0 + b_1x + b_2x^2 + \cdots)$$
$$= a_0b_0 + (a_0b_1 + a_1b_0)x + (a_0b_2 + a_1b_1 + a_2b_0)x^2 + \cdots.$$

The degree of the polynomial p is just the greatest integer k for which the coefficient of x^k is nonzero. Then p is monic iff the coefficient of x^k is 1. We can think of the nonzero numbers as being polynomials of degree 0. The numbers $a_0, a_1, a_2, \ldots$ are called the *coefficients* of the polynomial $a_0 + a_1x + a_2x^2 + \cdots$. (Sometimes this polynomial is denoted $p(x)$ instead of p.) For consistency in our arguments we put $x^0 = 1$. Our first result is known as the *Euclidean algorithm*.

Theorem 1. *Let p and q be nonzero polynomials. Then there exist unique polynomials r and s satisfying $p = rq + s$ such that either $s = 0$ or degree $s <$ degree q.*

PROOF. The proof of existence is by induction on degree p. For degree $p = 0$, we can set $r = 0$ and $s = p$ if degree $q > 0$, or we can set $s = 0$ and $r = pq^{-1}$ if degree $q = 0$.

Now suppose $n =$ degree p and that the conclusion is valid for any polynomial p_1 for which degree $p_1 < n$. Let $m =$ degree q. Without loss of generality we can assume that $m \leq n$; otherwise we can set $r = 0$ and $s = p$. Let a and b be numbers such that $ax^n + p$ does not have degree n and $bx^m + q$ does not have degree m. Then $a \neq 0$, $b \neq 0$ and the polynomial $p - ab^{-1}x^{n-m}q$ does not have degree n. Explain (Problem 2). Then either $p = ab^{-1}x^{n-m}q$ or degree $(p - ab^{-1}x^{n-m}q) < n$. Why? (See Problem 2.) In the event that $p = ab^{-1}x^{n-m}q$ we set $r = ab^{-1}x^{n-m}$ and $s = 0$, and the proof is complete. In the event that degree $(p - ab^{-1}x^{n-m}q) < n$, there exists (by the inductive hypothesis) polynomials r_1 and s such that $p - ab^{-1}x^{n-m}q = r_1q + s$ where either $s = 0$ or degree $s <$ degree q. Then $p = (ab^{-1}x^{n-m} + r_1)q + s$ and we set $r = ab^{-1}x^{n-m} + r_1$. This proves existence.

To prove uniqueness suppose also that r_0 and s_0 are polynomials such that $p = r_0q + s_0$ and either $s_0 = 0$ or degree $s_0 <$ degree q. Then $rq + s = r_0q + s_0$ and $(r - r_0)q = s_0 - s$. Since either $s_0 - s = 0$ or degree $(s_0 - s) <$ degree q we must have $r - r_0 = 0$. Then $s_0 - s = 0$ and $s = s_0$, $r = r_0$.

We say that a nonzero polynomial q *divides* a polynomial p if there exists a polynomial r such that $p = rq$. If $p \neq 0$, then degree $p =$ degree $q +$ degree r and degree $p \geq$ degree q. A polynomial p is without constant term iff x divides p. Why? (Problem 4.) If p and q are nonzero polynomials each dividing the other, then $p = r_1q$, $q = r_2p$, $q = r_2r_1q$, degree $(r_2r_1) = 0$, and the polynomials r_1 and r_2 are nonzero numbers. If q divides p_1 and q divides p_2, then q divides $p_1 + p_2$ and $p_1 - p_2$, because $p_1 = r_1q$ and $p_2 = r_2q$ imply

$p_1 \pm p_2 = (r_1 \pm r_2)q$. If q divides p and if p_1 is any nonzero polynomial, then q divides $p_1 p$ because $p = rq$ implies $p_1 p = (p_1 r)q$.

By an *irreducible* polynomial we mean a polynomial p with
degree $p > 0$ such that p is divided by no polynomial q satisfying
$0 < $ degree $q < $ degree p. For example, every polynomial of degree
1 is irreducible. Why? (Problem 13.)

Theorem 2.   *Any monic polynomial p of positive degree is the product
of monic irreducible polynomials.*

PROOF. The proof is by induction on degree p. If degree
$p = 1$ then p is irreducible and we can take p to be the only factor.
Assume that the conclusion is true of any polynomial of degree $<$
degree p. We can also assume without loss of generality that p is not
irreducible. Then $p = qr$ where $0 < $ degree $q < $ degree p. Since
degree $q + $ degree $r = $ degree p we also have $0 < $ degree $r < $ degree
p. By replacing q and r with cq and $c^{-1}r$ (where c is an appropriate
number) if necessary, we can assume that both q and r are monic.
By the inductive hypothesis there exist monic irreducible poly-
nomials $q_1, \ldots, q_n, r_1, \ldots, r_m$ such that $q = q_1 \cdots q_n, r = r_1 \cdots r_m$,
and $p = qr = q_1 \cdots q_n r_1 \cdots r_m$, which completes the proof.

Theorem 3.   *The factorization of p given in Theorem 2 is unique in
the following sense; if $p = p_1 \cdots p_n = q_1 \cdots q_m$ where the p_i and q_j are
monic irreducible polynomials, then for any monic irreducible polynomial q,
the number of indices i satisfying $p_i = q$ equals the number of indices j
satisfying $q_j = q$.*

PROOF. The proof is by induction on degree p. For degree
$p = 1$ the result is clear. Assume that the conclusion is valid for
polynomials of degree $<$ degree p but invalid for p. Then $p_1 \neq q_j$ for
each $j = 1, \ldots, m$; for otherwise $p_2 \cdots p_n = q_1 \cdots q_{j-1}q_{j+1} \cdots q_m$
and the conclusion would be false for this polynomial, contrary to
the inductive hypothesis. Likewise $q_1 \neq p_i$ for each $i = 1, \ldots, n$.

For the sake of definiteness let degree $p_1 \leq $ degree q_1. Put
$k = $ degree $q_1 - $ degree p_1; then $q_1 \neq x^k p_1$ and degree $(q_1 - x^k p_1) <$
degree q_1. Select a number a such that $a(q_1 - x^k p_1)$ is monic.
Since p_1 divides $q_1 \cdots q_m$ and $x^k p_1 q_2 \cdots q_m$, we have that p_1
divides the monic polynomial $a(q_1 - x^k p_1)q_2 \cdots q_m$; say $rp_1 =
a(q_1 - x^k p_1)q_2 \cdots q_m$. By factoring r we obtain a factorization of
rp_1 in which p_1 is a factor. But p_1 does not divide $a(q_1 - x^k p_1)$
because p_1 does not divide q_1. By factoring $a(q_1 - x^k p_1)$ we obtain
a factorization of rp_1 in which p_1 is not a factor. Hence the factorization of rp_1 is not unique. But degree $(rp_1) = $ degree $[a(q_1 - x^k p_1)] +$
degree $(q_2 \cdots q_m) < $ degree p, contrary to assumption. This
completes the proof.

If p is a polynomial and c is a number, we let $p(c)$ denote the
number formed by replacing x with c in p. To wit, $p(c) = a_0 +
a_1 c + a_2 c^2 + \cdots + a_n c^n$ where $p = a_0 + a_1 x + a_2 x^2 + \cdots + a_n x^n$.

Theorem 4. *Let p be a polynomial of positive degree and let c be a number. Then $x - c$ divides $p - p(c)$. Furthermore, $x - c$ divides p iff $p(c) = 0$.*

PROOF. We first prove by induction on n that $x - c$ divides $x^n - c^n$. This is clear for $n = 1$. For $n = 2$ we have $(x - c)(x + c) = x^2 - c^2$. Now suppose n is an integer > 2 and assume that $x - c$ divides $x^m - c^m$ for each $m < n$. Then $x - c$ divides $(x + c) \times (x^{n-1} - c^{n-1}) - cx(x^{n-2} - c^{n-2}) = x^n - c^n$. This completes the induction.

Now let $p = a_0 + a_1x + a_2x^2 + \cdots + a_nx^n$. It follows that $x - c$ divides $(a_0 - a_0) + a_1(x - c) + a_2(x^2 - c^2) + \cdots + a_n \times (x^n - c^n) = p - p(c)$. In particular, if $p(c) = 0$ then $x - c$ divides p. On the other hand if $x - c$ divides p, then $x - c$ divides $p - (p - p(c)) = p(c)$; hence $p(c) = 0$ because degree $(x - c) = 1 > 0$.

If we use real numbers only, the polynomial $x^2 + 1$ is irreducible. We argue by contradiction; suppose $x^2 + 1$ is not irreducible. Then $x^2 + 1$ is divided by a monic polynomial of degree 1, say $x + a$. By Theorem 4, $(-a)^2 + 1 = 0$. But this is impossible because $a^2 \geq 0$. In Lecture 2-2, Problem 6, we will show that any irreducible polynomial has degree 1 or 2 if we restrict ourselves to real numbers.

If $p(c) = 0$, or equivalently, $x - c$ divides p, we say that c is a *zero* of the polynomial p or a *root* of the equation $p(x) = 0$. The *Fundamental Theorem of Algebra* states that any polynomial of positive degree has a complex zero. We will henceforth assume this statement to be true, since a proof is beyond the scope of our book. Most texts on complex analysis provide a proof. A proof by more elementary techniques is given in "Algebra of Matrices" by Malcolm F. Smiley [12], pp. 52–53. It follows that any irreducible polynomial with complex coefficients has degree 1. Hence if p is a monic polynomial of degree n, Theorem 2 shows that there exist complex numbers $a_1, \ldots, a_n$ such that

$$p = (x - a_1) \cdots (x - a_n).$$

By Theorem 4 each a_i is a root of p. Now if b is a root of p, then $x - b$ divides p and $x - b$ must be one of the factors $x - a_i$ by an argument in the proof of Theorem 3 (Problem 3). Hence $a_i = b$ for some i. In particular, the polynomial p cannot have more than n distinct roots.

Problems for Lecture 1—2

1. Prove in detail that $a_0 + a_1x + a_2x^2 + \cdots + a_nx^n = (a_0, a_1, a_2, \ldots)$.

2. In the proof of Theorem 1 explain why $p - ab^{-1}x^{n-m}q$ does not have degree n. Explain why either $p - ab^{-1}x^{n-m}q = 0$ or degree $(p - ab^{-1}x^{n-m}q) < n$.

3. Let $q_1, \ldots, q_n$ and p be irreducible monic polynomials such that p divides $q_1 \cdots q_n$. Prove that there exists an index j such that $q_j = p$.

4. Prove that a polynomial p is without constant term iff x divides p.

5. Let P be a (possibly infinite) family of monic polynomials. Let M denote the family of all polynomials of the form $q_1 p_1 + \cdots + q_n p_n$ where the q_i are polynomials and the $p_i \in P$.

    (a) Show that the sum and difference of any two polynomials in M is in M.

    (b) Show that the product of any polynomial with a polynomial in M is in M.

    (c) Let q be a monic polynomial such that $q \in M$ and no nonzero polynomial in M has lower degree than q. Show that q divides all the polynomials in P. (Hint: use the Euclidean algorithm on the polynomials q and p.)

    (d) Show that any polynomial in M is divided by q.

    (e) Let r be a polynomial that divides every polynomial in P. Prove that r divides every polynomial in M. In particular, show there exists a polynomial s such that $sr = q$.

    (f) Suppose that $q = 1$. Prove that there exist polynomials $q_1, \ldots, q_n$ and $p_1, \ldots, p_n \in P$ such that $1 = q_1 p_1 + \cdots + q_n p_n$. Prove that the only polynomials that divide all the polynomials in P have degree 0.

6. Let P be a (possibly infinite) family of monic polynomials all of which are divisors of a fixed polynomial.

    (a) Let q_1 be a monic polynomial of lowest degree of which every member of P is a divisor. If q_2 is another polynomial of which every member of P is a divisor, prove that q_1 divides q_2. (Hint: use the Euclidean algorithm on q_1 and q_2.)

    (b) Suppose P consists of just two monic polynomials p and p_1, and define q and q_1 as in 5(c) and 6(a). Prove that $p p_1 = q q_1$. (Hint: if r is a polynomial of positive degree such that $p p_1 / q = r q_1$, show that rq divides both p and p_1 which is impossible.)

    (c) Use Theorems 2 and 3 to prove part (b).

7. By direct computation prove that $(p + q)(c) = p(c) + q(c)$ and $(pq)(c) = p(c)q(c)$ for any number c and any polynomials p and q.

8. In this problem we employ real numbers only. Prove that $x^2 + ax + b$ is irreducible iff $a^2 < 4b$.

9. For a complex number $a + bi$ (where a, b are real) we define *conjugate* $(a + bi)$ (written $\overline{a + bi}$) to be $a - bi$. Prove that if c is a complex root of a polynomial p with real coefficients, then $\bar{c}$ is also a root of p. Prove that if degree p is odd, then p has at least one real root.

10. Let c be a complex number. Prove that among the polynomials with real coefficients there is a unique monic irreducible polynomial p for which $p(c) = 0$. If q is a nonzero polynomial satisfying $q(c) = 0$, prove that p divides q. (Hint: c is a root of the polynomial $(x - c)(x - \bar{c}) = x^2 - (c + \bar{c})x + c\bar{c}$.)

11. Prove that for any positive integer n, $x + c$ divides $x^{2n-1} + c^{2n-1}$. (Hint: use induction on n and observe that

$$x^{2n-1} + c^{2n-1} = [x^2 + c^2][x^{2n-3} + c^{2n-3}] - x^2c^2[x^{2n-5} + c^{2n-5}].)$$

12. Let $a_0, a_1, \ldots, a_n$ be real numbers with $n > 0$, $a_0 \neq 0$, $a_n \neq 0$. Prove the inequality

$$\sum_{j,k=0}^{n} a_j a_k r^{j+k} \cos(j\theta - k\theta) \geq 0$$

for any real numbers r and θ. Use the Fundamental Theorem of Algebra to prove that there exists at least one choice of r and θ such that equality holds and $r \neq 0$, $0 \leq \theta < \pi$. Prove that there exist not more than n such choices of r and θ.

13. Prove that every polynomial of degree 1 is irreducible.

$\mathcal{L}$ecture 1–3

Vector Spaces and Linear Combinations. We begin with the definition of a *complex vector space*. In this definition, by a *scalar* we mean a complex number.

Definition 1. *By a complex vector space we mean a nonvoid set of elements called vectors such that the following hold.*

For vectors v_1 and v_2 there exists a vector $v_1 + v_2$ (called the sum of v_1 and v_2) such that

(1) $v_1 + (v_2 + v_3) = (v_1 + v_2) + v_3$ *for any vectors v_1, v_2, and v_3,*

(2) $v_1 + v_2 = v_2 + v_1$ *for any vectors v_1 and v_2,*

(3) *there is a vector 0 such that $v + 0 = v$ for any vector v. (We denote the zero vector and the zero scalar by the same symbol; they can be distinguished by the context.)*

(4) *for each vector v there exists a vector $-v$ such that $v + (-v) = 0$.*

For any vector v and any scalar c there exists a vector cv (called the product of c and v) such that

(5) $c(v_1 + v_2) = cv_1 + cv_2$ *for any vectors v_1 and v_2 and any scalar c,*

(6) $(c_1 + c_2)v = c_1v + c_2v$ *for any scalars c_1 and c_2 and any vector v,*

(7) $(c_1c_2)v = c_1(c_2v)$ *for any scalars c_1 and c_2 and any vector v,*

(8) $1v = v$ *for any vector v.*

A *real vector space* is defined in the same way if by a *scalar* we mean a real number. Before proceeding to develop the properties of vector spaces, we present several examples. That each of the following structures does satisfy the properties (1) to (7) is left to the reader to prove (Problem 1). When we do not specify whether a vector space V is real or complex, we understand that V could be either.

1. Let V consist of one vector we call 0. Put $0 + 0 = 0$ and $c0 = 0$ for any scalar c.

2. Let V be the set of all scalars, and for addition and multiplication take the usual operations defined on the scalars.

3. The complex numbers form a real vector space under the usual addition and multiplication of complex numbers.

4. Fix an integer $n > 0$ and let V consist of all ordered n-tuples of scalars. Addition and multiplication is componentwise; to wit,

$$(a_1, \ldots, a_n) + (b_1, \ldots, b_n) = (a_1 + b_1, \ldots, a_n + b_n)$$

and

$$c(a_1, \ldots, a_n) = (ca_1, \ldots, ca_n).$$

This space is known as *real Euclidean n-space* when we use real scalars, or *complex Euclidean n-space* when we use complex scalars.

5. Fix an integer $n > 0$ and let V consist of all polynomials with degree $< n$, together with the 0 polynomial. For addition and multiplication we take the usual operations on polynomials (see Lecture 1-2).

6. Let V consist of all polynomials with scalar coefficients, and define addition and multiplication in the usual way on polynomials.

7. Let V consist of all the continuous scalar valued functions on the real line and define addition and multiplication by the usual operations on functions. (For this example the notion of continuity is needed.)

We can draw the following conclusions about any vector space V. If v, $w \in V$ and $v + w = 0$, then $-v + (v + w) = -v = (-v + v) + w = 0 + w = w$ and $w = -v$. If $v \in V$, then $0v = (0 + 0)v = 0v + 0v$ and $0 = -0v + 0v = (-0v + 0v) + 0v$ and $0v = 0$. If c is a scalar, then $c0 = c(0 + 0) = c0 + c0$, $0 = -c0 + c0 = (-c0 + c0) + c0$, and $c0 = 0$. The product of a nonzero scalar c with a nonzero vector v is a nonzero vector; for if $cv = 0$, then $0 = c^{-1}(cv) = 1v = v$ contrary to hypothesis. If $v \in V$, then $v + (-v) = 0$ and hence $-(-v) = v$. If c is a scalar and $v \in V$, then $0 = (c + (-c))v = cv + (-c)v = c(v + (-v)) = cv + c(-v)$ and hence $-cv = c(-v) = (-c)v$. Also $(-c)(-v) = cv$. If $v, w \in V$, we write $v - w$ for $v + (-w)$. Then the only vector x satisfying $x + w = v$ is $v - w$.

By a *linear combination* of the vectors $z_1, \ldots, z_n \in V$ we mean a vector v for which there exist scalars $c_1, \ldots, c_n$ satisfying $v = c_1 z_1 + \cdots + c_n z_n$. By a *scalar multiple* of the vector $z \in V$ we just mean a linear combination of the single vector z; to wit, a vector of the form cz for some scalar c. Plainly 0 is a scalar multiple of any vector, and 0 is the only scalar multiple of 0. The vector space V is said to be *finite dimensional* if there exists a finite set of vectors Z such that any vector in V is a linear combination of the vectors in Z. In this event Z is said to *generate* (or *span*) V, and Z is called a *generating* set of V. In the event V does not have a finite generating set we say that V is *infinite dimensional*. We shall consider infinite dimensional vector spaces only in Part 4 of this book. So in Parts 2, 3, and 5 we will assume that all vector spaces are finite dimensional.

The examples 1 to 5 just given are finite dimensional. In Example 1 the vector 0 spans V, and in Example 2 any nonzero vector spans V (Problem 2). (A vector space containing a nonzero vector is called *nonzero*.) A generating set for V in 3 is $\{1, i\}$. In

Example 4 the vectors $e_1 = (1, 0, \ldots)$, $e_2 = (0, 1, 0, \ldots)$, $\ldots$, $e_n = (0, \ldots, 0, 1)$ form a generating set of V. And in Example 5 the polynomials $1, x, x^2, \ldots, x^{n-1}$ span V.

However in Example 6, V is infinite dimensional. For if $p_1, \ldots, p_n$ are finitely many polynomials in V, then no polynomial of degree exceeding all the integers, degree $p_1, \ldots$, degree p_n, is a linear combination of $p_1, \ldots, p_n$. Likewise, we shall show in Part 2 that V is infinite dimensional in Example 7.

To every real vector space V there is related a complex vector space called the *complexification* of V (denoted $V + iV$). The vectors of $V + iV$ are ordered pairs (v_1, v_2) of vectors in V. Addition of vectors and scalar multiplication is defined $(v_1, v_2) + (v_3, v_4) = (v_1 + v_3, v_2 + v_4)$ and $(a + bi)(v_1, v_2) = (av_1 - bv_2, av_2 + bv_1)$ where $v_1, v_2, v_3, v_4 \in V$ and a, b are real. The verification of Properties (1) to (4) is simple; the zero vector is $(0, 0)$. The verification of Properties (5) to (8) is also simple, but we sketch a proof of Property (7) since it is slightly subtler than the others (Problem 3). If a_1, a_2, b_1, b_2 are real and $v_1, v_2 \in V$, then

$$(a_1 + b_1 i)[(a_2 + b_2 i)(v_1, v_2)] = (a_1 + b_1 i)(a_2 v_1 - b_2 v_2, a_2 v_2 + b_2 v_1)$$

$$= (a_1 a_2 v_1 - a_1 b_2 v_2 - b_1 a_2 v_2 - b_1 b_2 v_1, a_1 a_2 v_2$$
$$+ a_1 b_2 v_1 + a_2 b_1 v_1 - b_1 b_2 v_2)$$

$$= ((a_1 a_2 - b_1 b_2) v_1 - (a_1 b_2 + a_2 b_1) v_2, (a_1 a_2 - b_1 b_2) v_2$$
$$+ (a_1 b_2 + a_2 b_1) v_1)$$

$$= [(a_1 a_2 - b_1 b_2) + (a_1 b_2 + a_2 b_1)i](v_1, v_2)$$

$$= [(a_1 + b_1 i)(a_2 + b_2 i)](v_1, v_2).$$

Employing a slight abuse of language we refer to the vector $(v, 0)$ as v where $v \in V$. Then $(v_1, v_2) = v_1 + iv_2$, and the rules of addition and multiplication given read

$$(v_1 + iv_2) + (v_3 + iv_4) = (v_1 + v_3) + i(v_2 + v_4),$$
$$(a + bi)(v_1 + iv_2) = (av_1 - bv_2) + i(bv_1 + av_2).$$

Problems for Lecture 1—3

1. Prove in detail that V is a vector space in each of the Examples 1 to 7.
2. Prove that any nonzero vector spans V in Example 2.
3. Show in detail that the complexification $V + iV$ of a real vector space V is a complex vector space.

4. Prove that the complexification $V + iV$ of a real vector space V is finite dimensional if V is finite dimensional. (Hint: let $\{z_1, \ldots, z_n\}$ be a finite generating set for V. Then if $v_1 = \sum_j a_j z_j$ and $v_2 = \sum_j b_j z_j$ we have $v_1 + iv_2 = \sum_j a_j z_j + i \sum_j b_j z_j = \sum_j (a_j + ib_j) z_j$ in $V + iV$.) Prove that V is finite dimensional if $V + iV$ is finite dimensional.

5. Let V be a nonvoid set of continuous real valued functions defined on the real line. If V consists of all functions having, in turn, each of the following properties, determine whether or not V is a (possibly infinite dimensional) real vector space under the usual operations of addition and multiplication of functions in each situation.

    (a) $f(0) = 0$ for each $f \in V$.

    (b) $f(1) = 1$ for each $f \in V$.

    (c) $\int_0^1 f = 0$ for each $f \in V$.

    (d) $f(0) + f(1) + f(2) + f(3) = 0$ for each $f \in V$.

    (e) $f(t) = f(1 - t)$ for each $f \in V$ and each real number t.

    (f) $\int_0^1 f(t) f(1 - t) dt = 0$ for each $f \in V$.

    (g) $\int_{-\infty}^{\infty} |f|^3 (1 + |f|)^{-2}$ is finite for each $f \in V$.

    (h) $\int_{-\infty}^{\infty} |f|^2 (1 + |f|)^{-3}$ is finite for each $f \in V$.

    (i) $\int_0^1 f$ is rational for each $f \in V$.

Part 2   MATRICES,
DETERMINANTS,
AND
OPERATORS

$\mathcal{L}$ecture 2–1

Introduction. In Part 1 we defined vector spaces, and developed polynomials and their properties, including the unique factorization of a polynomial into the product of irreducible factors. In the present part we discuss bases of a vector space, matrices, determinants, direct sums, and quotient spaces, and we define (linear) operators on vector spaces. The classic results on bases and dimension are discussed in Lecture 2-2. In Lecture 2-4 singular and nonsingular matrices, ranks of matrices, eigenvalues, and eigenvectors of matrices are discussed. In Lecture 2-5 determinants of square matrices are defined by means of alternating multilinear forms, and the uniqueness of the parity of a permutation is established by employing the existence of a nontrivial such form. Cramer's rule and the expansion of a determinant by minors are developed in the list of problems for Lecture 2-5. Application of the notion of rank of a matrix to systems of linear equations is given in the problem list for Lecture 2-4. In these problem lists we also show that a nonsingular matrix is the product of elementary matrices, and that a matrix with determinant 1 is the product of commutators. Finally, in Lecture 2-6 we show how an operator on a vector space with a given basis defines a matrix, and how a matrix, together with a vector space with a given basis, defines an operator on this vector space.

$\mathcal{L}$*ecture* 2–2

Linear Dependence, Bases, and Subspaces. We say that the vectors $z_1, \ldots, z_n$ in a vector space V are *linearly dependent* if there exist scalars $a_1, \ldots, a_n$, not all 0, such that $a_1 z_1 + \cdots + a_n z_n = 0$. On the other hand we say that the vectors $z_1, \ldots, z_n$ are *linearly independent* if $a_1 z_1 + \cdots + a_n z_n = 0$ implies that $a_i = 0$ for each i. In other words, $z_1, \ldots, z_n$ are linearly independent if the only linear combination of them equal to the zero vector is the linear combination in which all the coefficients are 0.

For example, the vectors $(1, -1, 1), (-1, 2, -2), (0, 3, -3)$ are linearly dependent in Euclidean 3-space because

$$3(1, -1, 1) + 3(-1, 2, -2) + (-1)(0, 3, -3) = (0, 0, 0).$$

On the other hand the vectors $(1, -1, 1), (-1, 2, -2)$ are linearly independent because

$$a_1(1, -1, 1) + a_2(-1, 2, -2) = (a_1 - a_2, -a_1 + 2a_2, a_1 - 2a_2)$$
$$= (0, 0, 0)$$

implies $a_1 - a_2 = a_1 - 2a_2 = 0$ and $a_1 = a_2 = 0$. Furthermore, $(1, 0, 0, 0), (0, 1, 0, 0), (0, 0, 1, 0), (0, 0, 0, 1)$ are linearly independent vectors in Euclidean 4-space because

$$a_1(1, 0, 0, 0) + a_2(0, 1, 0, 0) + a_3(0, 0, 1, 0) + a_4(0, 0, 0, 1)$$
$$= (a_1, a_2, a_3, a_4) = (0, 0, 0, 0)$$

implies $a_1 = a_2 = a_3 = a_4 = 0$.

The vector z is linearly independent iff $z \neq 0$. This follows from the fact that $az = 0$ iff either the scalar $a = 0$ or the vector $z = 0$. If $z_i = z_j$ for some distinct indices i and j, then $z_1, \ldots, z_n$ are linearly dependent because $1z_i + (-1)z_j + \sum_{k \neq i, k \neq j} 0z_k = 0$. Similarly if one of the $z_i = 0$, then $z_1, \ldots, z_n$ are linearly dependent because $1z_i + \sum_{k \neq i} 0z_k = 0$.

Now suppose V is generated by one vector w; i.e., every vector in V is a scalar multiple of w. Then $z_1, \ldots, z_n$ are linearly dependent if $n > 1$. For if $z_1 \neq 0, z_2 \neq 0$, then $z_1 = a_1 w, z_2 = a_2 w$ where a_1, a_2 are nonzero scalars and $a_2 z_1 + (-a_1)z_2 + \sum_{k>2} 0z_k = a_1 a_2 w - a_1 a_2 w = 0$.

Whether or not the vectors $z_1, \ldots, z_n$ are linearly independent is unaffected by writing these vectors in a different order. To see this suppose $i_1, \ldots, i_n$ are the integers $1, \ldots, n$ in a different order. Then $a_1 z_1 + \cdots + a_n z_n = b_1 z_{i_1} + \cdots + b_n z_{i_n}$ where $b_1 = a_{i_1}, \ldots,$ $b_n = a_{i_n}$. If $a_i \neq 0$ for some i, then $b_j \neq 0$ for some j, and conversely.

Lemma 1. *The vectors $z_1, \ldots, z_n$ are linearly dependent iff there is an index i such that z_i is a linear combination of $z_1, \ldots, z_{i-1}$.*

PROOF. If $z_i = \sum_{j=1}^{i-1} a_j z_j$ for some scalars a_j, then $\sum_{j=1}^{i-1} a_j z_j + (-1) z_i + \sum_{j=i+1}^{n} 0 z_j = 0$ and the vectors $z_1, \ldots, z_n$ are linearly dependent. On the other hand if $\sum_{j=1}^{n} a_j z_j = 0$ where not all the scalars $a_j = 0$, let i be the greatest index for which $a_i \neq 0$. Then $z_i = \sum_{j=1}^{i-1} (-a_i^{-1} a_j) z_j$.

We say that a finite set of vectors Z in V is linearly dependent iff $z_1, \ldots, z_n$ are linearly dependent where $\{z_1, \ldots, z_n\}$ is an enumeration of Z (it makes no difference which enumeration). Otherwise Z is said to be linearly independent. For consistency in our arguments we say that the void set is linearly independent. In Lecture 2-6 we shall have occasion to discuss finite ordered sets; i.e., sets of vectors for which we use the order in which the vectors are listed.

We say that an infinite set of vectors is linearly dependent iff it has a linearly dependent finite subset. Equivalently, the set Z of vectors is linearly dependent iff there exist distinct vectors $z_1, \ldots,$ $z_n \in Z$ and scalars $c_1, \ldots, c_n$, not all 0, such that $c_1 z_1 + \cdots + c_n z_n = 0$. Otherwise we say that Z is linearly independent.

Theorem 1. *Let $z_1, \ldots, z_n$ be linearly independent vectors in V, and let $z_1, \ldots, z_n, w$ be linearly dependent for some vector $w \in V$. Then w is a linear combination of the $z_1, \ldots, z_n$.*

PROOF. There exist scalars $c_1, \ldots, c_n$ and a, not all 0, such that $\sum_i c_i z_i + aw = 0$. Clearly $a \neq 0$; for if $a = 0$, then not all the $c_i = 0$ and $z_1, \ldots, z_n$ are linearly dependent, contrary to assumption. Finally, we have $w = \sum_i - a^{-1} c_i z_i$.

Theorem 2. *Let $z_1, \ldots, z_n$ be linearly independent vectors in V and let $c_2, \ldots, c_n$ be scalars. Then the vectors $z_2 - c_2 z_1, \ldots, z_n - c_n z_1$ are linearly independent.*

PROOF. Suppose $a_2, \ldots, a_n$ are scalars such that

$$\sum_{i=2}^{n} a_i (z_i - c_i z_1) = 0 = \sum_{i=2}^{n} a_i z_i - \left(\sum_{i=2}^{n} a_i c_i \right) z_1.$$

Then all the $a_i = 0$ because $z_1, \ldots, z_n$ are linearly independent. Hence the vectors $z_2 - c_2 z_1, \ldots, z_n - c_n z_1$ are linearly independent.

By a *subspace* of a vector space V we mean a nonvoid subset U of V satisfying

(1) $z_1 + z_2 \in U$ if $z_1 \in U$ and $z_2 \in U$,
(2) $cz \in U$ if $z \in U$ and c is scalar.

It is easy to see (Problem 1) that U is a vector space in its own right under the addition and scalar multiplication defined on V. The vector space axioms hold in U because they hold in V. (Note that if $z \in U$, then $z + (-z) \in U$ and $0 \in U$.) In particular, V is a subspace of V, and the singleton set (0) is a subspace of V. A subspace U of V other than (0) is called a *nonzero* subspace of V, and a subspace U other than V is called a *proper* subspace of V. Subspaces naturally give rise to the following question: We assume that V has a finite generating set; but must any subspace U of V have a finite generating set? Theorem 4 will answer this question in the affirmative. The problem is not simple, because vectors in a generating set of V might not lie in U.

Lemma 2.   *Let W be a nonvoid (possible infinite) set of vectors in a vector space V and let U denote the set of all linear combinations of vectors in W. Then*

(1)   *U is a subspace of V and $W \subset U$,*

(2)   *if U_0 is a subspace of V such that $W \subset U_0$, then $U \subset U_0$.*

PROOF.   Let $w_1, \ldots, w_n$ be vectors in W and consider the linear combinations $\sum_i a_i w_i$ and $\sum_i b_i w_i$. Then $\sum_i a_i w_i + \sum_i b_i w_i = \sum_i (a_i + b_i) w_i \in U$. If c is a scalar, then $c(\sum_i a_i w_i) = \sum_i a_i c w_i \in U$. Thus U is a subspace of V. Furthermore, any vector in W is a linear combination of vectors in W, and $W \subset U$. This establishes (1).

Now suppose U_0 is a subspace of V such that $W \subset U_0$. If $w_1, \ldots, w_n \in W$, then $a_i w_i \in U_0$ for each i (where a_i is a scalar), and $a_1 w_1 + a_2 w_2 \in U_0$, $a_1 w_1 + a_2 w_2 + a_3 w_3 \in U_0, \ldots, \sum_i a_i w_i \in U_0$. Hence $U \subset U_0$, and (2) is proved.

Incidentally, we see that W generates U. We call U the subspace of V spanned (or generated) by the set of vectors W.

Theorem 3.   *The vectors $z_1, \ldots, z_n \in V$ are linearly dependent if V is generated by a set containing fewer than n vectors.*

PROOF.   Suppose the set $\{w_1, \ldots, w_m\}$ spans V and $m < n$. The proof will be by induction on m. If $m = 1$, then every vector in V is a scalar multiple of w_1 and the conclusion is obvious. Now assume that the result is true of vector spaces spanned by a set of $m - 1$ vectors. Let U denote the subspace spanned by the vectors $w_1, \ldots, w_{m-1}$. For each index $i = 1, \ldots, n$ there exists a scalar c_i such that $z_i + c_i w_m \in U$. Why? (Problem 2.) We can assume without loss of generality that not all the $c_i = 0$; for otherwise $z_i \in U$ for each i, and the conclusion follows from the inductive hypothesis applied to U. To save notation let $c_1 \neq 0$. For each $i = 2, \ldots, n$ we have

$$(z_i + c_i w_m) - c_i c_1^{-1}(z_1 + c_1 w_m) = z_i - c_i c_1^{-1} z_1 \in U.$$

By the inductive hypothesis applied to U, we have that the vectors $z_2 - c_2 c_1^{-1} z_1, \ldots, z_n - c_n c_1^{-1} z_1$ are linearly dependent because

$n - 1 > m - 1$. Then the vectors $z_1, \ldots, z_n$ are linearly dependent by Theorem 2.

Theorem 4. *Let Z be a (possibly void) finite linearly independent subset of a subspace U of a vector space V, and let W be a (possibly infinite) set generating U. Then there exists a (possibly void) finite subset X of W, disjoint from Z, such that $Z \cup X$ is a linearly independent set generating U.*

PROOF. Suppose V is generated by a set of n vectors. Let $\mathscr{E}$ denote the family of all subsets E of $W - Z$ for which $Z \cup E$ is linearly independent. For example, the void set is in $\mathscr{E}$. By Theorem 3, no set in $\mathscr{E}$ has more than n vectors. Let X be a set in $\mathscr{E}$ such that no set in $\mathscr{E}$ has more vectors than does X. Suppose $w \in W - (Z \cup X)$. Then $X \cup \{w\} \notin \mathscr{E}$ and $Z \cup X \cup \{w\}$ is linearly dependent. But $Z \cup X$ is linearly independent, so w lies in the span of $Z \cup X$ by Theorem 1. Hence every vector in W is in the span of $Z \cup X$. Since W spans U, so must $Z \cup X$ span U. This completes the proof.

We now see that any subspace U of V is finite dimensional, i.e., has a finite generating set. To prove this, just let Z be void and $W = U$ in Theorem 4. We make the

Definition 1. *A basis of a vector space V is a linearly independent set generating V. We let the void set be the basis of the vector space with one vector 0.*

From Theorems 3 and 4 we see that any subspace of V has a finite basis. If V has two bases Z and W, then by Theorem 3, W has at least as many vectors as Z. Reversing the roles of Z and W we see that they have the same number of vectors. All bases of V are finite, and all have the same number of vectors. We make the

Definition 2. *By the dimension of V we mean the number of vectors in a basis of V, denoted $\dim V$. If $\dim V = n$ we say that V is n-dimensional.*

From Theorems 3 and 4 we see that any linearly independent subset Z of V can be extended to a basis by adjoining vectors to Z. Indeed, if W is a given set generating V, then we can extend Z to a basis by adjoining vectors in W. A basis can be extracted from any set W generating V; to see this just let Z be void in Theorem 4.

Theorem 5. *Let U be a subspace of V. Then $\dim U \le \dim V$, and equality holds iff $U = V$.*

PROOF. Let Z be a basis of U. We can extend Z to a basis Z_0 of V. Now $\dim U \le \dim V$ because Z does not contain more vectors than Z_0.

But if $\dim U = \dim V$, then $Z = Z_0$ and this set is a basis of both U and V. Thus V is spanned by a set of vectors in U, and every vector in V is in U. Hence $U = V$.

Theorem 6.   *Let $\{z_1, \ldots, z_n\}$ be a finite set of vectors in V.   Then the following are equivalent.*

(1) *$\{z_1, \ldots, z_n\}$ is a basis of V,*

(2) *each vector in V is a unique linear combination of the vectors $z_1, \ldots, z_n$.*

PROOF.   Assume (1).   Then $\{z_1, \ldots, z_n\}$ spans V because it is a basis.   If $v \in V$ is a vector and a_i, b_i are scalars such that $v = \sum_i a_i z_i = \sum_i b_i z_i$, then $\sum_i (a_i - b_i) z_i = 0$.   Hence $a_i - b_i = 0$ and $a_i = b_i$ for each i because $\{z_1, \ldots, z_n\}$, as a basis, is a linearly independent set.

Assume (2).   Then $\{z_1, \ldots, z_n\}$ generates V.   If a_i are scalars such that $\sum_i a_i z_i = 0$, then $a_i = 0$ for each i because the vector 0 can be represented as $\sum_i 0 z_i$.   Hence $\{z_1, \ldots, z_n\}$ is linearly independent and is a basis of V.

For an example of a basis consider the vectors $e_1 = (1, 0, \ldots, 0)$, $e_2 = (0, 1, 0, \ldots, 0)$, $e_3 = (0, 0, 1, 0, \ldots, 0)$, etc., in Euclidean n-space.   For any vector $v = (a_1, \ldots, a_n)$ we have $v = a_1 e_1 + \cdots + a_n e_n$, and v is the zero vector iff $a_i = 0$ for each i.   This proves that $\{e_1, \ldots, e_n\}$ is a basis of Euclidean n-space, and the dimension of this space is n.

Theorem 7.   *Let $V + iV$ be the complexification of a real vector space V.   Then*

(1) *a subset Z of V is linearly independent in V iff Z is linearly independent in $V + iV$.*

(2) *a subset Z of V is a basis of V iff Z is a basis of $V + iV$.*

PROOF.   For $z_1, \ldots, z_n \in V$ and for real scalars a_j and b_j, we have $0 = \sum_j (a_j + ib_j) z_j = \sum_j a_j z_j + i(\sum_j b_j z_j)$ iff $\sum_j a_j z_j = \sum_j b_j z_j = 0$.   Conclusion (1) follows immediately from this (Problem 3).

If $v_1 = \sum_j a_j z_j$, $v_2 = \sum_j b_j z_j$, then $v_1 + iv_2 = \sum_j (a_j + ib_j) z_j$.   Conclusion (2) follows immediately (Problem 3).

Problems for Lecture 2—2

1. Prove that a subspace U of a vector space V is a vector space.

2. In the proof of Theorem 3 show why there exist scalars c_i such that $z_i + c_i w_m \in U$.

3. Complete the proof of Theorem 7.

4. Let ξ denote a (possibly infinite) family of subspaces of a vector space V.   Prove that $\bigcap_{U \in \xi} U$ is a subspace of V.

5. Prove that the vector space composed of all polynomials of degree $<n$ has dimension n.   (Hint: show that $\{1, x, x^2, \ldots, x^{n-1}\}$ is a basis.)

6. Show that the complex numbers form a 2-dimensional real vector space under the usual operations of addition and multiplication. Prove that a complex number z is the root of a polynomial (with real coefficients) of degree 1 or 2. Hence every irreducible polynomial with real coefficients has degree 1 or 2. Why?

7. Prove that any subset of a linearly independent set of vectors in V is linearly independent.

8. If w is in the span of the vectors $z_1, \ldots, z_n$, but not in the span of $z_2, \ldots, z_n$, prove that z_1 is in the span of $w, z_2, \ldots, z_n$.

9. Let V be an n-dimensional space. Prove that there exists a 1–1 mapping f of V onto Euclidean n-space such that $f(a_1 z_1 + a_2 z_2) = a_1 f(z_1) + a_2 f(z_2)$ for any scalars a_1, a_2 and any $z_1, z_2 \in V$. (Hence V is "like" Euclidean n-space. The reason we consider vector spaces other than Euclidean n-space is to show that our results do not depend on a particular choice of a basis or "coordinate system.")

10. Let V be Euclidean n-space, and for each nonzero vector $z = (a_1, \ldots, a_n) \in V$ let $j(z)$ denote the smallest index i for which $a_i \neq 0$. Let $e_i \in V$ be the vector which is 1 in the i-th place and 0 in every other place. Prove

    (a) that if $z_1, \ldots, z_m$ are vectors satisfying $j(z_i) < j(z_{i+1})$ for each $i = 1, \ldots, m - 1$, then $z_1, \ldots, z_m$ are linearly independent.

    (b) that if U is a subspace of V, then there exists an ordered basis $\{z_1, \ldots, z_m\}$ of U such that $j(z_i) < j(z_{i+1})$ for each $i = 1, \ldots, m - 1$, and the $j(z_i)$-th entry of z_k is 0 for $k \neq i$.

    (c) if $e_i \in U$ and if $\{z_1, \ldots, z_m\}$ is a basis of U as given in (b), then one of the vectors z_j is a scalar multiple of e_i.

    (d) We perform an *elementary operation* on the ordered basis $\{w_1, \ldots, w_m\}$ of U by writing $w_i + c w_j$ in place of w_i for some scalar c and some indices i, j $(i \neq j)$. Show that the new set $\{w_1, \ldots, w_{i-1}, w_i + c w_j, w_{i+1}, \ldots, w_m\}$ thus formed is also a basis of U. Show that we can construct an ordered basis $\{z_1, \ldots, z_m\}$ as in (b) by performing an elementary operation on $\{w_1, \ldots, w_m\}$, then performing an elementary operation on the resulting basis, then performing another elementary operation on the next resulting basis, and so on, and finally reordering the vectors in the last basis constructed, if necessary. If $U = V$ show that z_i must be a scalar multiple of e_i for each i.

$\mathcal{L}ecture$ 2–3

Direct Sums and Quotient Spaces. Let z be a vector in the vector space V, let U be a set of vectors in V. By $z + U$ we mean the set of vectors $\{z + u : u \in U\}$. Now let $U_1, U_2, \ldots, U_m$ be subsets of the vector space V. By $U_1 + U_2 + \cdots + U_m$ we mean the set of vectors $\{\sum_{i=1}^{m} z_i : z_i \in U_i \text{ for each } i\}$.

If $U_1, U_2, \ldots, U_m$ are subspaces of V, then $U_1 + U_2 + \cdots + U_m$ is a subspace of V. To see this, observe that if c is a scalar and $z_i \in U_i$, $w_i \in U_i$, then

$$(z_1 + z_2 + \cdots + z_m) + (w_1 + w_2 + \cdots + w_m)$$
$$= (z_1 + w_1) + (z_2 + w_2) + \cdots + (z_m + w_m)$$

and $c(z_1 + z_2 + \cdots + z_m) = cz_1 + cz_2 + \cdots + cz_m$.

Theorem 1. *Let $U_1, U_2, \ldots, U_m$ be subspaces of V. Then the following are equivalent.*
(1) *If $z_i, w_i \in U_i$ for each $i = 1, 2, \ldots, m$, such that $\sum_{i=1}^{m} z_i = \sum_{i=1}^{m} w_i$, then $z_i = w_i$ for each $i = 1, 2, \ldots, m$.*
(2) *If $z_i \in U_i$ for each $i = 1, 2, \ldots, m$ such that $\sum_{i=1}^{m} z_i = 0$, then $z_i = 0$ for each $i = 1, 2, \ldots, m$.*

PROOF. Assume (2). Then if $z_i, w_i \in U_i$ for each $i = 1, 2, \ldots, m$ and $\sum_{i=1}^{m} z_i = \sum_{i=1}^{m} w_i$, we have $\sum_{i=1}^{m} (z_i - w_i) = 0$. But $z_i - w_i \in U_i$ for each $i = 1, 2, \ldots, m$, and $z_i - w_i = 0$ for each $i = 1, 2, \ldots, m$ by (2).

Assume (1). Then if $z_i \in U_i$ for each $i = 1, 2, \ldots, m$ and $\sum_{i=1}^{m} z_i = 0$, we have $\sum_{i=1}^{m} w_i = 0$ where $w_i = 0 \in U_i$ for each $i = 1, 2, \ldots, m$. So $z_i = w_i = 0$ for each $i = 1, 2, \ldots, m$ by (1).

In effect, (1) says that a vector in $U_1 + U_2 + \cdots + U_m$ can be written in only one way as a sum of vectors in U_i. If (1) and (2) hold we say that the U_i are *linearly independent* and that $U_1 + U_2 + \cdots + U_m$ is the *direct sum* of the subspaces U_i; this direct sum is commonly written $U_1 \oplus U_2 \oplus \cdots \oplus U_m$ or $\sum_{i=1}^{m} \oplus U_i$. If U and W are subspaces of V such that $V = U \oplus W$, we say that U and W are *complementary* subspaces of V. We also say that W is *complementary* to U, and U is *complementary* to W. For any subspace U of V there is a complementary subspace. To see this extend a basis $\{u_1, \ldots, u_m\}$ of U to a basis $\{u_1, \ldots, u_m, w_1, \ldots, w_n\}$ of V. Then the subspace spanned by the vectors $w_1, \ldots, w_n$ is complementary to U (Problem 1).

Theorem 2. *Let $U_1, U_2, \ldots, U_m$ be subspaces of V. We have*
(1) *If $V = U_1 + U_2 + \cdots + U_m$ and* $\dim V = \dim U_1 + \dim$
$U_2 + \cdots + \dim U_m$, *then* $V = U_1 \oplus U_2 \oplus \cdots \oplus U_m$.
(2) *If $U_1, U_2, \ldots, U_m$ form a direct sum, then* $\dim \left(\sum_{i=1}^{m} \oplus U_i \right) = \sum_{i=1}^{m} \dim U_i$.

PROOF. For each index $i = 1, 2, \ldots, m$, let $\{z_{i1}, z_{i2}, \ldots\}$ be a basis of U_i. Then the vectors in the set $\bigcup_{i=1}^{m} \{z_{i1}, z_{i2}, \ldots\}$ span $U_1 + U_2 + \cdots + U_m$. Why? (Problem 16.)

In (1) we have that V is spanned by the vectors in the set $\bigcup_{i=1}^{m} \{z_{i1}, z_{i2}, \ldots\}$ and there are precisely $\dim V$ of these vectors. Hence $\bigcup_{i=1}^{m} \{z_{i1}, z_{i2}, \ldots\}$ is a basis of V. If $u_i \in U_i$ for each $i = 1, 2, \ldots, m$ and $\sum_{i=1}^{m} u_i = 0$, then $u_i = \sum_j a_{ij} z_{ij}$ for some scalars a_{ij} for each index i, and $0 = \sum_{i=1}^{m} u_i = \sum_i \left(\sum_j a_{ij} z_{ij} \right) = \sum_{ij} a_{ij} z_{ij}$, and $a_{ij} = 0$ for each i and each j. It follows that $u_i = 0$ for each i and the U_i form a direct sum.

In (2), if a_{ij} are scalars satisfying $\sum_{ij} a_{ij} z_{ij} = 0$, then $0 = \sum_i \left(\sum_j a_{ij} z_{ij} \right)$, $\sum_j a_{ij} z_{ij} = 0$ for each i, and $a_{ij} = 0$ for each i and each j. Thus the vectors z_{ij} are linearly independent and $\bigcup_{i=1}^{m} \{z_{i1}, z_{i2}, \ldots\}$ is a basis of $U_1 \oplus U_2 \oplus \cdots \oplus U_m$. It follows that $\dim \left(\sum_{i=1}^{m} \oplus U_i \right) = \sum_{i=1}^{m} \dim U_i$.

Theorem 3. *If $U_1, U_2, \ldots, U_m$ are subspaces of V, and if W is a subspace of V satisfying $U_i \subset W$ for each $i = 1, \ldots, m$, then $U_1 + U_2 + \cdots + U_m \subset W$. Furthermore, $U_i \subset U_1 + U_2 + \cdots + U_m$ for each i.*

PROOF. Suppose $u_i \in U_i$ for each $i = 1, 2, \ldots, m$. Then $u_i \in W$ for each $i = 1, \ldots, m$, and $\sum_{i=1}^{m} u_i \in W$. This proves that $U_1 + U_2 + \cdots + U_m \subset W$.

If a vector $u_i \in U_i$ for some index i, then $u_1 + u_2 + \cdots + u_m \in U_1 + U_2 + \cdots + U_m$ where $u_j = 0$ for each $j \neq i$. Hence $U_i \subset U_1 + U_2 + \cdots + U_m$. This completes the proof.

If U and W are subspaces of V, then $U \cap W$ is also a subspace. For if c is scalar and $z_1, z_2 \in U \cap W$, then $cz_1 \in U \cap W$ and $z_1 + z_2 \in U \cap W$. Note that if U_1 is another subspace such that $U_1 \subset U$, and $U_1 \subset W$, then $U_1 \subset U \cap W$. For any subspace U we have $U + (0) = U = U \oplus (0)$ and $U \cap (0) = (0)$.

Theorem 4. *Suppose U and W are subspaces of a vector space V. Then* $\dim (U + W) + \dim (U \cap W) = \dim U + \dim W$.

PROOF. Suppose $\dim U = n$, $\dim W = m$, and $\dim (U \cap W) = q$. We must prove that $n + m - q = \dim (U + W)$. Let $\{z_1, \ldots, z_q\}$ be a basis of $U \cap W$. Extend this set to a basis $\{z_1, \ldots, z_q, u_{q+1}, \ldots, u_n\}$ of U. Extend $\{z_1, \ldots, z_q\}$ to a basis $\{z_1, \ldots, z_q, w_{q+1}, \ldots, w_m\}$ of W. It suffices to show that the set $\{z_1, \ldots, z_q, u_{q+1}, \ldots, u_n, w_{q+1}, \ldots, w_m\}$ is a basis of $U + W$. Clearly this set spans $U + W$

because it contains a basis of U and a basis of W. To prove linear independence suppose we have scalars a_i, b_i, c_i such that

$$a_1 z_1 + \cdots a_q z_q + b_{q+1} u_{q+1} + \cdots + b_n u_n$$
$$+ c_{q+1} w_{q+1} + \cdots + c_m w_m = 0.$$

Then

$$a_1 z_1 + \cdots + a_q z_q + b_{q+1} u_{q+1} + \cdots + b_n u_n = -c_{q+1} w_{q+1} - \cdots - c_m w_m$$

is a vector in $U \cap W$, and there exist scalars d_i such that $d_1 z_1 + \cdots + d_q z_q + c_{q+1} w_{q+1} + \cdots + c_m w_m = 0$. Since $\{z_1, \ldots, z_q, w_{q+1}, \ldots, w_m\}$ is linearly independent we have that each $c_i = 0$ and each $d_i = 0$. Hence $a_1 z_1 + \cdots + a_q z_q + b_{q+1} u_{q+1} + \cdots + b_n u_n = 0$. Since $\{z_1, \ldots, z_q, u_{q+1}, \ldots, u_n\}$ is linearly independent we have that each $a_i = 0$ and each $b_i = 0$. This completes the proof.

Let U be a subspace of a vector space V. By a *coset* we mean $z + U$ for some vector $z \in V$. In particular $z \in z + U$, because $z = z + 0$ and $0 \in U$. If $z_1 \in z + U$, then $z_1 - z = u \in U$, and $z_1 + U = z_1 + (z - z_1) + U = z + U$ (Problem 2). Hence each vector in V lies in one and only one coset. In other words, V is the union of all the cosets, and the intersection of any two distinct cosets is void.

We define the sum of two cosets as follows: $(z_1 + U) + (z_2 + U) = z_1 + z_2 + U$. This definition is well-posed, for if $w_1 + U = z_1 + U$, $w_2 + U = z_2 + U$, then $z_1 - w_1 \in U$, $z_2 - w_2 \in U$, $(z_1 - w_1) + (z_2 - w_2) = (z_1 + z_2) - (w_1 + w_2) \in U$ and $z_1 + z_2 + U = w_1 + w_2 + U$. We define scalar multiplication of cosets as follows; $c(z + U) = cz + U$. This definition is well-posed, for if $z + U = w + U$, then $z - w \in U$, $c(z - w) \in U$, $cz - cw \in U$, and $cz + U = cw + U$.

We claim that under the addition and scalar multiplication just defined, the cosets form a vector space whose zero vector is the coset U. To see this make the following observations:

$$z_1 + U + (z_2 + U + z_3 + U) = z_1 + (z_2 + z_3) + U$$
$$= (z_1 + z_2) + z_3 + U = (z_1 + U + z_2 + U) + z_3 + U,$$
$$z_1 + U + z_2 + U = z_1 + z_2 + U$$
$$= z_2 + z_1 + U = z_2 + U + z_1 + U,$$
$$z + U + U = z + U,$$
$$(z + U) + (-z + U) = U,$$
$$c(z_1 + U + z_2 + U) = c(z_1 + z_2 + U) = c(z_1 + z_2) + U$$
$$= cz_1 + cz_2 + U = cz_1 + U + cz_2 + U,$$
$$(c_1 + c_2)(z + U) = (c_1 + c_2)z + U = c_1 z + U + c_2 z + U,$$
$$(c_1 c_2)(z + U) = (c_1 c_2)z + U = c_1(c_2 z) + U$$
$$= c_1(c_2 z + U) = c_1[c_2(z + U)],$$
$$1(z + U) = 1z + U = z + U.$$

The vector space of cosets is often called the *quotient space* V *modulo* U, written V/U. We have

Theorem 5. *Let U be a subspace of the vector space V. Then* $\dim V = \dim U + \dim V/U$.

PROOF. Let $\dim U = q$ and let $\dim V = n$. Extend a basis $\{u_1, \ldots, u_q\}$ of U to a basis $\{u_1, \ldots, u_q, z_{q+1}, \ldots, z_n\}$ of V. It suffices to prove that the cosets $z_{q+1} + U, \ldots, z_n + U$ form a basis of V/U. For any coset $z + U$, there exist scalars a_i, b_j such that $z = \sum_i a_i u_i + \sum_j b_j z_j$, $z - \sum_j b_j z_j \in U$, and $z + U = \sum_j b_j (z_j + U)$. Hence the vectors $z_{q+1} + U, \ldots, z_n + U$ span V/U. Now assume b_j are scalars such that $\sum_j b_j (z_j + U) = U$. Then $\sum_j b_j z_j \in U$ and $\sum_j b_j z_j$ is a linear combination of the u_i. Since $\{u_1, \ldots, u_q, z_{q+1}, \ldots, z_n\}$ is linearly independent, each $b_j = 0$. This completes the proof.

Problems for Lecture 2—3

1. Let U be a subspace of a vector space V. Extend a basis $\{u_1, \ldots, u_q\}$ of U to a basis $\{u_1, \ldots, u_q, w_1, \ldots, w_n\}$ of V. Prove that the subspace of V spanned by the vectors $w_1, \ldots, w_n$ is complementary to U.

2. Prove that if U is a subspace of V, and $u \in U$, then $u + U = U$.

3. Construct a vector space V with nonzero subspaces U_1, U_2, U_3 such that U_2 is complementary to U_3, U_1 is complementary to U_2, and U_3 is complementary to U_1. Can $\dim V$ be odd? Explain.

4. Let $U_1, \ldots, U_m$ be linearly dependent (not independent) subspaces of a vector space V. Prove that there exists an index i such that $U_i \cap (U_1 + \cdots + U_{i-1}) \neq (0)$. Are $U_1/(U_1 \cap U_2)$ and $U_2/(U_1 \cap U_2)$ necessarily linearly independent subspaces of $V/(U_1 \cap U_2)$? Explain.

5. Let U be a subspace of V and let W be a subspace of U. Prove that U/W is a subspace of V/W and show that the dimension of the quotient space V/W modulo U/W is the same as the dimension of V/U.

6. Let U and W be subspaces of the vector space V. Prove that the quotient spaces $(U + W)/W$ and $U/(U \cap W)$ have the same dimension.

7. If U_1, U_2, U_3 are subspaces of V and $U_2 \subset U_1$, prove that $U_1 \cap (U_2 + U_3) = U_2 + U_1 \cap U_3$.

8. Prove that Euclidean n-space is the direct sum $U_1 \oplus U_2 \oplus \cdots \oplus U_n$ where U_i denotes the subspace composed of all vectors whose j-th coordinate $(j \neq i)$ is 0.

9. Let $U_1, U_2, \ldots, U_m$ be subspaces of a vector space V such that $(0) \neq U_1 \subset U_2 \subset \cdots \subset U_m = V$. Prove that there exists a subspace W_i of U_i for each $i = 1, 2, \ldots, m$ such that $U_i = W_1 \oplus W_2 \oplus \cdots \oplus W_i$ for each $i = 1, 2, \ldots, m$.

10. Let $U_1, U_2, \ldots, U_m$ be subspaces of a vector space V such that $V = \sum_{i=1}^{m} \oplus U_i$, and let each U_i be the direct sum of finitely many subspaces $W_{i1}, W_{i2}, \ldots$. Prove that $V = \sum_{ij} \oplus W_{ij}$.

11. Let U_1 and U_2 be subspaces of a vector space V. Prove that $U_1 \cup U_2 = U_1 + U_2$ iff either $U_1 \subset U_2$ or $U_2 \subset U_1$. Prove that $U_1 \cup U_2 = V$ iff either $U_1 = V$ or $U_2 = V$.

12. Let U_1 and U_2 be subspaces of a vector space V such that $\dim U_1 = 5$, $\dim U_2 = 8$, and $\dim (U_1 + U_2)/(U_1 \cap U_2) = 3$. Find $\dim (U_1 + U_2)$ and $\dim (U_1 \cap U_2)$. Can we have $\dim U_1 = 5$, $\dim U_2 = 8$, and $\dim (U_1 + U_2)/(U_1 \cap U_2) = 4$? Explain.

13. Let U_1 and U_2 be subspaces of a vector space V such that $\dim (U_1 + U_2)/U_2 = 6$, $\dim (U_1 + U_2)/U_1 = 5$, and $\dim (U_1 \cap U_2) = 3$. Find $\dim U_1$ and $\dim U_2$.

14. Let U_1 and U_2 be subspaces of Euclidean 9-space, let $\dim U_1 = 6$, $\dim U_2 = 8$. Prove that $\dim (U_1 \cap U_2) \geq 5$.

15. Throughout this problem let U_1, U_2, U_3 be subspaces of V.

   (a) Prove that $U_1 + (U_2 + U_3) = (U_1 + U_2) + U_3$ and $U_1 \cap (U_2 \cap U_3) = (U_1 \cap U_2) \cap U_3$.

   (b) Prove that $\dim U_1 = \dim [(U_1 + U_2) \cap (U_1 + U_3)] + \dim (U_1 \cap U_3) - \dim [(U_1 + U_2) \cap U_3]$.

   (c) Prove that $\dim (U_1 \cap U_2) + \dim [(U_1 + U_2) \cap U_3] = \dim (U_1 \cap U_3) + \dim [(U_1 + U_3) \cap U_2]$.

   (d) Prove that $U_1 \cap U_2 + U_1 \cap U_3 \subset U_1 \cap (U_2 + U_3)$ and show by example that equality need not hold.

   (e) Prove that $U_1 \cap (U_2 + U_3) = (0)$ implies $(U_1 + U_2) \cap (U_1 + U_3) = U_1$.

   (f) Prove that $2 \dim (U_1 + U_2 + U_3) \leq \dim (U_1 + U_2) + \dim (U_1 + U_3) + \dim (U_2 + U_3)$, and show that equality holds iff U_1, U_2, U_3 are linearly independent. (Hint: in (f) show that $\dim (U_1 + U_2 + U_3) \leq \dim (U_1 + U_2) + \dim (U_1 + U_3) - \dim U_1$, then find two other inequalities by interchanging the roles of U_1, U_2, U_3, and add the three inequalities.)

   (g) Prove that

   $$2(\dim U_1 + \dim U_2 + \dim U_3)$$
   $$\geq 3[\dim (U_1 \cap U_2) + \dim (U_2 \cap U_3)$$
   $$+ \dim (U_3 \cap U_1) - \dim (U_1 \cap U_2 \cap U_3)],$$

   and show that equality holds iff $U_1 = U_2 = U_3$.

(Hint: in (g) show that $\dim (U_1 \cap U_2 \cap U_3) \geq \dim (U_1 \cap U_2) + \dim (U_2 \cap U_3) - \dim (U_1 + U_3) = \dim (U_1 \cap U_2) + \dim (U_2 \cap U_3) + \dim (U_3 \cap U_1) - \dim U_1 - \dim U_3$, then find two other inequalities by interchanging the roles of U_1, U_2, U_3, and add the three inequalities.)

16. In the first paragraph of the proof of Theorem 2, why must the set $\bigcup_{i=1}^{m} \{z_{i1}, z_{i2}, \ldots\}$ span $U_1 + U_2 + \cdots + U_m$?

$\mathcal{L}$ecture 2–4

Matrices. By an n by m *matrix* we mean a rectangular array of scalars having n (horizontal) rows and m (vertical) columns. For example, $\begin{bmatrix} 1 & 2 & 3 \\ -5 & i & 4i \end{bmatrix}$ is a 2 by 3 matrix, $[-5i]$ is a 1 by 1 matrix, and $[1 \quad 2 \quad 3 \quad i \quad -i]$ is a 1 by 5 matrix. We say that an n by m matrix is *square* if $n = m$. Among these matrices, only $[-5i]$ is square. Also $\begin{bmatrix} 2 & 3 \\ -i & 17 \end{bmatrix}$ is square. By the *main diagonal* of a square n by n matrix we mean the set of i-th row, i-th column positions $(i = 1, \ldots, n)$ in the matrix. For example, the entries on the main diagonal of the last mentioned matrix are 2 and 17. The *super diagonal* of a square n by n matrix is the diagonal above the main diagonal; that is, the set of i-th row, $(i + 1)$-th column positions $(i = 1, \ldots, n - 1)$ in the matrix. For example, the entries on the super diagonal of $\begin{bmatrix} 1 & 4 & 1 \\ 0 & 2 & 5 \\ 2 & i & 3 \end{bmatrix}$ are 4 and 5. By the ij-th entry of a matrix, we mean the entry in the i-th row and j-th column. Sometimes a matrix A, whose ij-th entry is a_{ij}, is denoted (a_{ij}) or $[a_{ij}]$. We say that a matrix is *real* if its entries are real scalars, *complex* if its entries are complex scalars.

Suppose (a_{ij}) and (b_{ij}) are n by n matrices. By $(a_{ij}) + (b_{ij})$ we mean the n by n matrix $(a_{ij} + b_{ij})$ whose ij-th entry is $a_{ij} + b_{ij}$. By $r(a_{ij})$ we mean the n by n matrix (ra_{ij}) if r is a scalar. By $(a_{ij})(b_{ij})$ we mean the n by n matrix whose ij-th entry is $\sum_{k=1}^{n} a_{ik}b_{kj}$. By I_n we mean the n by n matrix all of whose main diagonal entries are 1, and all of whose other entries are 0. By the matrix 0 we mean the matrix whose every entry is 0. (This is the third "zero" we have considered; the 0 scalar, the 0 vector, and now the 0 matrix. However, they can always be distinguished by the context.) We say that two matrices are equal if they are identical; i.e., their corresponding entries coincide. For n by n matrices we have $AI_n = I_nA = A$ and $A + 0 = 0 + A = A$. This can be verified by direct computation.

32

Theorem 1.   *For all n by n matrices A, B, C and all scalars r, s we have*

(1) $(A + B) + C = A + (B + C)$.

(2) $A + 0 = 0 + A = A$.

(3) *For every A there is a unique n by n matrix $-A$ such that $A + (-A) = (-A) + A = 0$.*

(4) $A + B = B + A$.

(5) $I_n A = AI_n = A$.

(6) $(AB)C = A(BC)$.

(7) $A(B + C) = AB + AC$.

(8) $(A + B)C = AC + BC$.

(9) $(rA)B = r(AB)$.

(10) $r(A + B) = rA + rB$.

(11) $(r + s)A = rA + sA$.

These properties can be checked by routine computation (Problem 2). We will sketch only the more difficult arguments. Let the ij-th entry of A be a_{ij}, of B be b_{ij}, of C be c_{ij}. Then the ij-th entry of BC is $\sum_{k=1}^{n} b_{ik} c_{kj}$. The ij-th entry of $A(BC)$ is

$$\sum_{h=1}^{n} a_{ih} \left(\sum_{k=1}^{n} b_{hk} c_{kj} \right) = \sum_{h,k} a_{ih} b_{hk} c_{kj}.$$

The ij-th entry of AB is $\sum_{k=1}^{n} a_{ik} b_{kj}$. The ij-th entry of $(AB)C$ is $\sum_{h=1}^{n} \left(\sum_{k=1}^{n} a_{ik} b_{kh} \right) c_{hj} = \sum_{h,k} a_{ik} b_{kh} c_{hj}$ and (6) is evident. To prove (7) observe that the ij-th entry of both $A(B + C)$ and $AB + AC$ is $\sum_{k=1}^{n} a_{ik}(b_{kj} + c_{kj}) = \sum_{k=1}^{n} a_{ik} b_{kj} + \sum_{k=1}^{n} a_{ik} c_{kj}$. Note also that the ij-th entry of $-A$ is $-a_{ij}$.

The properties (1) to (11) are valid when the matrices A, B, C are replaced by scalars. Matrices, however, do lack some properties of scalars. For example,

$$\begin{bmatrix} 1 & 0 \\ 0 & 0 \end{bmatrix}\begin{bmatrix} 0 & 1 \\ 0 & 0 \end{bmatrix} = \begin{bmatrix} 0 & 1 \\ 0 & 0 \end{bmatrix} \quad \text{and} \quad \begin{bmatrix} 0 & 1 \\ 0 & 0 \end{bmatrix}\begin{bmatrix} 1 & 0 \\ 0 & 0 \end{bmatrix} = \begin{bmatrix} 0 & 0 \\ 0 & 0 \end{bmatrix}.$$

Thus, for n by n matrices, AB might be 0 even though $A \neq 0$ and $B \neq 0$. Furthermore, we might have $AB \neq BA$. If $AB = BA$ we say that A and B *commute*. If $AB = 0$ and $A \neq 0$, $B \neq 0$, then there cannot exist an n by n matrix A^{-1} satisfying $A^{-1}A = I_n$; for if such a matrix A^{-1} exists, we have $A^{-1}(AB) = A^{-1}0 = 0 = (A^{-1}A)B = I_n B = B$, which is impossible.

If A is an n by m matrix with ij-th entry a_{ij} we can regard each row of A as a vector in Euclidean m-space. The i-th row is the vector $(a_{i1}, a_{i2}, \ldots, a_{im})$. Likewise each column of A can be regarded as a vector in Euclidean n-space. The j-th column is the vector $(a_{1j}, a_{2j}, \ldots, a_{nj})$.

Theorem 2.   *Let A and B be n by n matrices, let the ij-th entry of A be a_{ij}, and let the ij-th entry of B be b_{ij}. Then the rows of AB are linear combinations of the rows of B, and the columns of AB are linear combinations of the columns of A. To wit, the i-th row of AB is $\sum_{j=1}^{n} a_{ij}z_j$ where $z_j = (b_{j1}, b_{j2}, \ldots, b_{jn})$, and the j-th column of AB is $\sum_{i=1}^{n} b_{ij}w_i$ where $w_i = (a_{1i}, a_{2i}, \ldots, a_{ni})$.*

PROOF.   The i-th row of AB is $(\sum_{k=1}^{n} a_{ik}b_{k1}, \sum_{k=1}^{n} a_{ik}b_{k2}, \ldots, \sum_{k=1}^{n} a_{ik}b_{kn})$ and this is evidently the vector $\sum_{k=1}^{n} a_{ik}z_k$. The j-th column of AB is $(\sum_{k=1}^{n} a_{1k}b_{kj}, \sum_{k=1}^{n} a_{2k}b_{kj}, \ldots, \sum_{k=1}^{n} a_{nk}b_{kj})$ and this is evidently the vector $\sum_{k=1}^{n} b_{kj}w_k$.

Let $z = (a_1, \ldots, a_n)$ and $w = (b_1, \ldots, b_n)$ be vectors in Euclidean n-space. By $z \cdot w$ we mean the scalar $\sum_{i=1}^{n} a_ib_i$. By the *annihilator* of the vector w we mean the set of all vectors z satisfying $z \cdot w = 0$. If W is a set of vectors in Euclidean n-space, by the *annihilator* of W we mean the set of all z satisfying $z \cdot w = 0$ for each $w \in W$. If z is in the annihilators of $w_1, \ldots, w_m$, it follows that $(\Sigma c_iw_i) \cdot z = \Sigma c_i(w_i \cdot z) = 0$, and z is in the annihilator of any linear combination of the w_i. It is clear that the annihilator of any set of vectors W is a subspace of Euclidean n-space (Problem 3).

Let A be an n by m matrix. By the *row space* of A we mean the subspace of Euclidean m-space spanned by the rows of A. By the *column space* of A we mean the subspace of Euclidean n-space spanned by the columns of A.

Theorem 3.   *Let A be an n by m matrix with row space Z and column space W. Then $\dim Z = \dim W$.*

PROOF.   Let a_{ij} be the ij-th entry of A, let $z_i = (a_{i1}, \ldots, a_{im})$ and $w_j = (a_{1j}, \ldots, a_{nj})$. Let $p = \dim Z$ and $q = \dim W$. Select a basis $z_{\pi(1)}, z_{\pi(2)}, \ldots, z_{\pi(p)}$ of Z and a basis $w_{\sigma(1)}, w_{\sigma(2)}, \ldots, w_{\sigma(q)}$ of W. If i is an index different from $\sigma(1), \sigma(2), \ldots \sigma(q)$, then w_i is a linear combination $c_{i1}w_{\sigma(1)} + c_{i2}w_{\sigma(2)} + \cdots + c_{iq}w_{\sigma(q)}$ of the $w_{\sigma(j)}$. Thus $-w_i + c_{i1}w_{\sigma(1)} + c_{i2}w_{\sigma(2)} + \cdots + c_{iq}w_{\sigma(q)} = 0$. An inspection of the components of both sides of this equation shows that the vector u_i, which is c_{ij} in the $\sigma(j)$-th place, -1 in the i-th place, and 0 in every other place, is in the annihilator of each z_j and is in the annihilator U of Z (Problem 4). Furthermore, the vectors u_i just constructed are linearly independent: if $\Sigma c_iu_i = 0$ where i runs over all indices different from $\sigma(1), \sigma(2), \ldots, \sigma(q)$, then the i-th entry of Σc_iu_i is $-c_i$, so $c_i = 0$ for each i.

Now let $u = (c_1, c_2, \ldots, c_n)$ be a vector in U. An inspection of components shows that $c_1w_1 + c_2w_2 + \cdots + c_nw_n = 0$. Now $u + \Sigma c_iu_i$ is also in U and for each index j different from $\sigma(1)$,

$\sigma(2), \ldots, \sigma(q)$, the j-th component of $u + \Sigma\, c_i u_i$ is 0. It follows that $u + \Sigma\, c_i u_i = 0$; otherwise the vectors $w_{\sigma(1)}, w_{\sigma(2)}, \ldots, w_{\sigma(q)}$ are linearly dependent. Explain (Problem 5). Thus the vectors u_i constitute a basis of U and dim $U = n - q$.

Let B be the p by n matrix whose rows are $z_{\pi(1)}, z_{\pi(2)}, \ldots, z_{\pi(p)}$. Then B also has row space Z and by the preceding argument the dimension of the column space of B is $n -$ dim U. But since the columns of B are vectors in Euclidean p-space, $n -$ dim $U = n - (n - q) = q \leq p$.

Now define the m by n matrix A^t as follows; the ij-th entry of A^t is a_{ji}. Clearly the row space of A^t is the column space of A and the column space of A^t is the row space of A. By the preceding argument applied to A^t we obtain $p \leq q$. Finally, $p = q$ and the proof is complete.

The m by n matrix constructed in the preceding paragraph is called the *transpose* of A (often denoted A^t, as before). The *rank* of A is defined to be the dimension of the row space (or column space) of A. Note that A and A^t have the same rank.

Theorem 4.   *If W is a subspace of Euclidean n-space, and if U is the annihilator of W, then* dim $U +$ dim $W = n$.

PROOF.   Let $w_1, \ldots, w_p$ be a basis of W and let A be the p by n matrix with rows $w_1, \ldots, w_p$. Then the rank of A is p and by the proof of Theorem 3, dim $U = n - p$.

If the rank of an n by n matrix A is n, we say that A is *nonsingular* (or invertible). If rank $A < n$ we say that A is *singular*.

Theorem 5.   *For an n by n matrix A the following are equivalent.*
(1) $AB = I_n$ *for some n by n matrix B.*
(2) $CA = I_n$ *for some n by n matrix C.*
(3) A *is nonsingular.*
In the event (1), (2), *and* (3) *hold, then $B = C$ and there is only one matrix B satisfying $AB = I_n$ or $BA = I_n$.*

PROOF.   Assume (3) holds. Then the row space of A is Euclidean n-space, and so is the column space of A. Let z_k denote the k-th row of A and let w_k denote the k-th column of A. Then $\{z_1, \ldots, z_n\}$ and $\{w_1, \ldots, w_n\}$ are both bases of Euclidean n-space. Let e_i denote the vector in Euclidean n-space which is 1 in the i-th place and 0 in every other place. There are scalars b_{ij} and c_{ij} such that $e_i = \sum_{k=1}^{n} c_{ik} z_k$ for each $i = 1, \ldots, n$, and $e_j = \sum_{k=1}^{n} b_{kj} w_k$ for each $j = 1, \ldots, n$. Let B be the matrix (b_{ij}) and let C be the matrix (c_{ij}). By Theorem 2 the j-th column of AB is e_j and the i-th row of CA is e_i. Clearly $AB = CA = I_n$, and we have proved (3) $\Rightarrow$ (1) and (3) $\Rightarrow$ (2).

Now assume (2). The rows e_i of I_n are linear combinations of the rows of A by Theorem 2, and consequently the row space of A

is Euclidean n-space. Thus A is nonsingular and we have proved $(2) \Rightarrow (3)$. Likewise, an argument on the columns of A (Problem 6) shows that $(1) \Rightarrow (3)$. Hence we have shown $(2) \Leftrightarrow (3) \Leftrightarrow (1)$.

Finally, assume that (1), (2), and (3) hold. Then $C = CI_n = C(AB) = (CA)B = I_nB = B$ and $B = C$. Furthermore, if $AB_1 = I_n$, then $B_1 = (BA)B_1 = B$; if $B_1A = I_n$, then $B_1 = B_1I_n = B_1(AB) = B$. This concludes the proof.

If A is nonsingular, we let A^{-1} denote the unique matrix satisfying $AA^{-1} = A^{-1}A = I_n$. We call A^{-1} the *inverse* of A.

For a square matrix A, we define A^2 to be AA, A^3 to be AA^2, and in general A^m to be AA^{m-1}. For consistency we define A^0 to be I_n. Let $p(x) = a_0 + a_1x + a_2x^2 + \cdots + a_mx^m$ be a polynomial with scalar coefficients. By $p(A)$ we mean the matrix formed by replacing x with the matrix A; thus, $p(A) = a_0I_n + a_1A + a_2A^2 + \cdots + a_mA^m$. If B commutes with A, then a simple argument by induction on m shows that B commutes with A^m (Problem 7; note that $BA^m = ABA^{m-1}$). Hence if B commutes with A, then

$$p(A)B = (a_0I_n + a_1A + \cdots + a_mA^m)B$$

$$= a_0B + a_1BA + \cdots + a_mBA^m = Bp(A),$$

and B commutes with $p(A)$. If B commutes with A and p and q are polynomials, then $q(B)$ commutes with $p(A)$. Why? (Problem 7.)

If $p(A) = 0$ we say that p *annuls* A. Note that if p and q are polynomials and if p annuls A, then pq annuls A (See Problem 21).

Under the operations of addition of matrices and scalar multiplication of a matrix, the n by n matrices form a vector space (Problem 9). Fix indices i and j and let A_{ij} denote the matrix which is 1 in the ij-th place and 0 in every other place. Together the matrices A_{ij} constitute a basis of the vector space of n by n matrices, and consequently this vector space has dimension n^2 (Problem 9).

Let M be a collection of n by n matrices and let A be an n by n matrix. By the symbol AM we mean the set $\{AB: B \in M\}$. Similarly MA means $\{BA: B \in M\}$. The equation $AM = MA$, for example, means that AM and MA are the same set of matrices. Similarly, $A + M$ means $\{A + B: B \in M\}$. If M and N are families of matrices, then NM means the set $\{AB: A \in N, B \in M\}$.

If A and B are n by n matrices, then by Theorem 2, the row space of AB is a subspace of the row space of B and the column space of AB is a subspace of the column space of A. Thus, rank $AB \leq$ rank B and rank $AB \leq$ rank A. If A is nonsingular, then rank $B = $ rank $A^{-1}(AB) \leq$ rank AB and rank $B = $ rank AB; if B is nonsingular, then rank $A = $ rank $(AB)B^{-1} \leq$ rank AB and rank $A = $ rank AB.

If A and B are n by n matrices and AB is nonsingular, then A and B are nonsingular; this follows from $n = \text{rank } AB \leq \text{rank } A$, $n = \text{rank } AB \leq \text{rank } B$. On the other hand, if A and B are nonsingular, then $(B^{-1}A^{-1})(AB) = B^{-1}(A^{-1}A)B = I_n$ and consequently AB is nonsingular with $(AB)^{-1} = B^{-1}A^{-1}$.

If A and B are n by n matrices we say that A is *similar* to B if there exists a nonsingular n by n matrix C satisfying $CAC^{-1} = B$. Every square matrix is similar to itself because $I_n A I_n^{-1} = A$. If A is similar to B, then $CAC^{-1} = B$ for some nonsingular C, $A = C^{-1}B(C^{-1})^{-1}$ and B is similar to A. If A is similar to B and B is similar to D, then $C_1 A C_1^{-1} = B$, $C_2 B C_2^{-1} = D$ for some nonsingular C_1 and C_2, and A is similar to D because $(C_2 C_1)A(C_2 C_1)^{-1} = C_2(C_1 A C_1^{-1})C_2^{-1} = C_2 B C_2^{-1} = D$. Consequently, similarity is an equivalence relation, and we can divide the n by n matrices into pairwise disjoint classes such that two matrices are similar iff they are in the same class. Matrices in the same class necessarily have the same rank. Why? (Problem 10.)

If A is an n by n matrix we say that the scalar a is an *eigenvalue* of A if $A - aI_n$ is singular. For example, 2 is an eigenvalue of $\begin{bmatrix} 1 & 1 \\ -1 & 3 \end{bmatrix}$ but 0 is not (Problem 11). If C is nonsingular we have rank $[C(A - aI_n)C^{-1}] = \text{rank } (CAC^{-1} - aI_n)$ and a is an eigenvalue of A iff a is an eigenvalue of CAC^{-1}. Thus similar matrices have the same eigenvalues. In Part 3 we will show that a square complex matrix must have a complex eigenvalue. However, a square real matrix need not have a real eigenvalue as the following example demonstrates.

Let A be the 2 by 2 matrix $\begin{bmatrix} 0 & 1 \\ -1 & 0 \end{bmatrix}$. Then if c is real, $A - cI_2 = \begin{bmatrix} -c & 1 \\ -1 & -c \end{bmatrix}$, and the row space of A contains the vectors $(-c, 1) - c(-1, -c) = (0, c^2 + 1)$, $(c^2 + 1)^{-1}(0, c^2 + 1) = (0, 1)$, and $-c(0, 1) - (-1, -c) = (1, 0)$. Hence, the row space of $A - cI_2$ is Euclidean 2-space and c is not an eigenvalue of A.

Let $B_1, B_2, \ldots, B_k$ be square matrices and suppose that for each $i = 1, \ldots, k$, B_i is n_i by n_i. By the *direct sum* $B_1 \oplus B_2 \oplus \cdots \oplus B_k$ we mean the $\sum_{i=1}^{k} n_i$ by $\sum_{i=1}^{k} n_i$ matrix formed by first writing B_1, then inserting B_2 immediately below and to the right of B_1, then inserting B_3 immediately below and to the right of B_2, and so on, until we insert B_k, and then filling all the remaining places with 0's.

For example, if $B_1 = \begin{bmatrix} 1 & 2 \\ 3 & 4 \end{bmatrix}$, $B_2 = [-7]$, $B_3 = \begin{bmatrix} 1 & 3 & -1 \\ 0 & 0 & 2 \\ 1 & -1 & 0 \end{bmatrix}$, then

$$B_1 \oplus B_2 \oplus B_3 = \begin{bmatrix} 1 & 2 & 0 & 0 & 0 & 0 \\ 3 & 4 & 0 & 0 & 0 & 0 \\ 0 & 0 & -7 & 0 & 0 & 0 \\ 0 & 0 & 0 & 1 & 3 & -1 \\ 0 & 0 & 0 & 0 & 0 & 2 \\ 0 & 0 & 0 & 1 & -1 & 0 \end{bmatrix},$$

$$B_3 \oplus B_1 = \begin{bmatrix} 1 & 3 & -1 & 0 & 0 \\ 0 & 0 & 2 & 0 & 0 \\ 1 & -1 & 0 & 0 & 0 \\ 0 & 0 & 0 & 1 & 2 \\ 0 & 0 & 0 & 3 & 4 \end{bmatrix}$$

Note that if A_i $(i = 1, \ldots, k)$ is an n_i by n_i matrix, then (Problem 12) we have

$$(A_1 B_1) \oplus \cdots \oplus (A_k B_k) = (A_1 \oplus \cdots \oplus A_k)(B_1 \oplus \cdots \oplus B_k)$$

and

$$(A_1 + B_1) \oplus \cdots \oplus (A_k + B_k) = (A_1 \oplus \cdots \oplus A_k) + (B_1 \oplus \cdots \oplus B_k).$$

Incidentally $A_1 \oplus \cdots \oplus A_k$ commutes with $B_1 \oplus \cdots \oplus B_k$ iff $A_i B_i = B_i A_i$ for each $i = 1, \ldots, k$ (Problem 12).

Problems for Lecture 2—4

1. Prove that for n by n matrices, we have $AI_n = I_n A = A$ and $A + 0 = 0 + A = A$.
2. Prove Theorem 1.
3. Prove that the annihilator of any set of vectors in Euclidean n-space is a subspace of Euclidean n-space.
4. In the proof of Theorem 3 show that u_i is in the annihilator of Z.
5. In the proof of Theorem 3 show that $u + \Sigma c_i u_i = 0$.
6. In the proof of Theorem 5 show that $(1) \Rightarrow (3)$.
7. Show that if A, B are n by n matrices that commute, then B commutes with A^m for any integer $m > 0$. Prove that $p(A)$ commutes with $q(B)$ for any polynomials p and q.
8. If p, q are polynomials, A is an n by n matrix, and p annuls A, prove that pq annuls A.

9. Prove that the n by n matrices form a vector space of dimension n^2.

10. Prove that similar matrices have the same rank. Must n by n matrices with the same rank be similar? Explain.

11. Show that 2 is an eigenvalue of $\begin{bmatrix} 1 & 1 \\ -1 & 3 \end{bmatrix}$ but 0 is not.

12. If A_i and B_i are n_i by n_i matrices, prove that

$$(A_1 \oplus \cdots \oplus A_k)(B_1 \oplus \cdots \oplus B_k) = (A_1 B_1) \oplus \cdots \oplus (A_k B_k)$$

and

$$(A_1 \oplus \cdots \oplus A_k) + (B_1 \oplus \cdots \oplus B_k) = (A_1 + B_1) \oplus \cdots \oplus (A_k + B_k).$$

Prove that $A_1 \oplus \cdots \oplus A_k$ commutes with $B_1 \oplus \cdots \oplus B_k$ iff $A_i B_i = B_i A_i$ for each i.

13. Show that the following matrices have the same rank.

$$\begin{bmatrix} a_1 & a_2 & a_3 \\ b_1 & b_2 & b_3 \\ c_1 & c_2 & c_3 \\ a_1 + b_1 & a_2 + b_2 & a_3 + b_3 \end{bmatrix}, \begin{bmatrix} a_1 & a_2 & a_3 \\ b_1 & b_2 & b_3 \\ c_1 & c_2 & c_3 \end{bmatrix},$$

$$\begin{bmatrix} a_2 + 2b_2 & a_3 + 2b_3 & a_1 + 2b_1 \\ b_2 - a_2 & b_3 - a_3 & b_1 - a_1 \\ c_2 + a_2 + b_2 & c_3 + a_3 + b_3 & c_1 + a_1 + b_1 \end{bmatrix}.$$

14. Show that the following matrices have the same rank.

$$\begin{bmatrix} a_1 & a_2 & a_3 & a_4 \\ b_1 & b_2 & b_3 & b_4 \\ c_1 & c_2 & c_3 & c_4 \end{bmatrix} \quad \begin{bmatrix} a_2 & b_2 & c_2 \\ a_3 & b_3 & c_3 \\ a_4 & b_4 & c_4 \\ a_1 & b_1 & c_1 \end{bmatrix}$$

15. Show that the following system of m equations in the unknowns $x_1, \ldots, x_n$

$$\begin{cases} a_{11}x_1 + a_{12}x_2 + \cdots + a_{1n}x_n = b_1 \\ a_{21}x_1 + a_{22}x_2 + \cdots + a_{2n}x_n = b_2 \\ \quad \cdot \qquad \cdot \qquad \qquad \cdot \qquad \cdot \\ \quad \cdot \qquad \cdot \qquad \qquad \cdot \qquad \cdot \\ \quad \cdot \qquad \cdot \qquad \qquad \cdot \qquad \cdot \\ a_{m1}x_1 + a_{m2}x_2 + \cdots + a_{mn}x_n = b_m \end{cases}$$

has a solution iff the matrices

$$\begin{bmatrix} a_{11}, & a_{12}, & \ldots, & a_{1n} \\ a_{21}, & a_{22}, & \ldots, & a_{2n} \\ \cdot & \cdot & & \cdot \\ \cdot & \cdot & & \cdot \\ \cdot & \cdot & & \cdot \\ a_{m1}, & a_{m2}, & \ldots, & a_{mn} \end{bmatrix} \qquad \begin{bmatrix} a_{11}, & a_{12}, & \ldots, & a_{1n}, & b_1 \\ a_{21}, & a_{22}, & \ldots, & a_{2n}, & b_2 \\ \cdot & \cdot & & \cdot & \cdot \\ \cdot & \cdot & & \cdot & \cdot \\ \cdot & \cdot & & \cdot & \cdot \\ a_{m1}, & a_{m2}, & \ldots, & a_{mn}, & b_m \end{bmatrix}$$

have the same rank.

16. Each solution $(\lambda_1, \ldots, \lambda_n)$ of the system of m homogeneous equations in n unknowns

$$\begin{cases} a_{11}x_1 + a_{12}x_2 + \cdots + a_{1n}x_n = 0 \\ a_{21}x_1 + a_{22}x_2 + \cdots + a_{2n}x_n = 0 \\ \cdot \qquad \cdot \qquad \qquad \cdot \\ \cdot \qquad \cdot \qquad \qquad \vdots \\ \cdot \qquad \cdot \qquad \qquad \cdot \\ a_{m1}x_1 + a_{m2}x_2 + \cdots + a_{mn}x_n = 0 \end{cases}$$

may be regarded as a vector in Euclidean n-space. Prove that the solutions form a subspace of Euclidean n-space of dimension n-rank A, where A is the m by n matrix whose ij-th entry is a_{ij}.

17. Let the vector z_0 in Euclidean n-space be a particular solution of the system

$$\begin{cases} a_{11}x_1 + a_{12}x_2 + \cdots + a_{1n}x_n = b_1 \\ \cdot \qquad \cdot \qquad \qquad \cdot \qquad \cdot \\ \cdot \qquad \cdot \qquad \qquad \cdot \qquad \cdot \\ \cdot \qquad \cdot \qquad \qquad \cdot \qquad \cdot \\ a_{m1}x_1 + a_{m2}x_2 + \cdots + a_{mn}x_n = b_m \end{cases}$$

Show that any solution of this system can be characterized as $z + z_0$ where z is a solution of the system of homogeneous equations

$$\begin{cases} a_{11}x_1 + a_{12}x_2 + \cdots + a_{1n}x_n = 0 \\ \cdot \qquad \cdot \qquad \qquad \cdot \\ \cdot \qquad \cdot \qquad \qquad \cdot \\ \cdot \qquad \cdot \qquad \qquad \cdot \\ a_{m1}x_1 + a_{m2}x_2 + \cdots + a_{mn}x_n = 0. \end{cases}$$

18. (a) Describe all the solutions of the system

$$\begin{cases} x_1 \quad\;\; + 2x_3 + 3x_4 = 2 \\ x_1 - x_2 + 2x_3 - 5x_4 = 1 \end{cases}$$

(b) For what real numbers c will the system

$$\begin{cases} x_1 + cx_2 + c^2x_3 + c^3x_4 = 1 \\ -x_1 + x_2 + cx_3 + c^2x_4 = -1 \\ \;\; x_1 + c^2x_2 + x_3 - x_4 = 1 \end{cases}$$

have *more than one* solution? Explain.

19. Let W denote the solution space of

$$\begin{cases} a_1x_1 + a_2x_2 = 0 \\ b_1x_1 + b_2x_2 = 0 \\ c_1x_1 + c_2x_2 = 0 \end{cases}$$

and let U denote the solution space of

$$\begin{cases} a_1x_1 + b_1x_2 + c_1x_3 = 0 \\ a_2x_1 + b_2x_2 + c_2x_3 = 0. \end{cases}$$

Prove that dim $U = 1 + $ dim W.

20. (a) Let U be a subspace of Euclidean n-space and let W denote the annihilator of U. Prove that dim $U + $ dim $W = n$. (Hint: Let $\{u_1, \ldots, u_p\}$ be a basis of U and consider the p by n matrix whose i-th row is u_i.)

(b) Let U_1, U_2 be subspaces of Euclidean n-space with $U_1 \subset U_2$, $U_1 \neq U_2$. Prove that the annihilator of U_2 is a proper subspace of the annihilator of U_1.

(c) Let W denote the annihilator of U. Prove that U is the annihilator of W. (Hint: Let U_1 denote the annihilator of W. Show that $U \subset U_1$ and dim $U = $ dim U_1.)

(d) Let W_1 be the annihilator of U_1 and W_2 be the annihilator of U_2. Prove that $W_1 + W_2$ is the annihilator of $U_1 \cap U_2$, and $W_1 \cap W_2$ is the annihilator of $U_1 + U_2$. (Hint: Let W be the annihilator of $U_1 \cap U_2$. Then $W_1 + W_2 \subset W$; if $W_1 + W_2 \neq W$, there is a vector v in the annihilator of $W_1 + W_2$ and not in $U_1 \cap U_2$ by (b). But v is in the annihilator of W_1, and the annihilator of W_2, and by (c) v is in U_1 and U_2.)

(e)   In (d) show that Euclidean n-space is the direct sum of U_1 and U_2 iff it is the direct sum of W_1 and W_2.

(f)   Suppose $\{z_1, \ldots, z_n\}$ is a basis of Euclidean n-space such that $z_i \cdot z_i = 1$ for each i and $z_i \cdot z_j = 0$ for $i \neq j$. Let $x = \sum_i a_i z_i$, $y = \sum_i b_i z_i$. Prove that $x \cdot y = \sum_i a_i b_i$. (Hint: Suppose $z_i = \sum_j c_{ij} e_j$, $\sum_j c_{ij}^2 = 1$ for each i, and $\sum_j c_{ij} c_{kj} = 0$ for $i \neq k$. Show that $x \cdot y = \sum_{ijk} a_i b_k c_{ij} c_{kj} = \sum_{ik} a_i b_k (\sum_j c_{ij} c_{kj})$.)

21. Let p and q be polynomials and let A be a square matrix. Prove that $(pq)(A) = p(A) q(A)$ and $(p + q)(A) = p(A) + q(A)$. Prove that $(cp)(A) = cp(A)$ for a scalar c.

22. If A and B are n by n matrices prove $(AB)^t = B^t A^t$. (Hint: compare the ij-th entry of $B^t A^t$ to the ji-th entry of AB.)

23. If C is a nonsingular n by n matrix, prove that C^t is nonsingular and $(C^t)^{-1} = (C^{-1})^t$. (Hint: by taking adjoints of both sides of the equation $CC^{-1} = I_n$ we obtain $(C^{-1})^t C^t = I_n$.)

24. Suppose A and B are similar n by n matrices. Prove that A^t is similar to B^t. (Hint: By taking adjoints of both sides of the equation $B = CAC^{-1}$ we obtain $B^t = (C^{-1})^t A^t C^t$.) Prove that $p(A)$ is similar to $p(B)$ for any polynomial p. (Hint: if C is nonsingular, show that $p(CAC^{-1}) = Cp(A)C^{-1}$.)

25. Let a_i be scalars such that the system of equations

$$\begin{cases} x + y = a_1 \\ x - y = a_2 \\ a_1 x + 2y = a_3 \end{cases}$$

has no solution in x, y. Prove that the system

$$\begin{cases} x + y + a_1 z = 1 \\ x - y + a_2 z = 3 \\ a_1 x + 2y + a_3 z = 9 \end{cases}$$

has a unique solution in x, y, z.

26. Let the a_i and b_i be real scalars. Find the rank of the matrix

$$\begin{bmatrix} a_1 & 0 & a_1 & b_1 & 1 \\ a_2 & 1 & 5 & b_2 & 0 \\ a_3 & 3 & 4 & b_3 & a_1 \end{bmatrix}.$$

Can we draw the same conclusion if the a_i and b_i are complex? Explain.

27.   Prove that there exists no complex number c such that the system of equations

$$\begin{cases} 3x + cy + 2z = 1 \\ 2x + 2cy + z = c^2 \\ cx + y + cz = c^4 \end{cases}$$

has more than one solution in x, y, z.

Lecture 2–5

Determinants. In this lecture we shall define a function mapping the set of square matrices into the set of scalars. This mapping is called the *determinant*. The determinant has many properties of great importance to our work in succeeding lectures. We begin with the

Definition 1. *By a k-form we mean a mapping f of the set of all ordered k-tuples of vectors in Euclidean n-space into the set of scalars that satisfies*

(1) $f(z_1, \ldots, z_{i-1}, cz_i, z_{i+1}, \ldots, z_k) = cf(z_1, \ldots, z_k)$ *for any scalar c and any index i.*

(2) $f(z_1, \ldots, z_{i-1}, z_i + z_i', z_{i+1}, \ldots, z_k)$
  $= f(z_1, \ldots, z_{i-1}, z_i, z_{i+1}, \ldots, z_k)$
  $\quad + f(z_1, \ldots, z_{i-1}, z_i', z_{i+1}, \ldots, z_k)$
  for any index i.

(3) $f(z_1, \ldots, z_k) = 0$ *if there exist indices i, j with $i \neq j$ and $z_i = z_j$.*

One example of a k-form is the mapping defined $f(z_1, \ldots, z_k) = 0$ for any vectors $z_1, \ldots, z_k$ in Euclidean n-space. We say that f is a *nontrivial* k-form if the range of f contains a nonzero scalar. Let $\{z_1, \ldots, z_n\}$ be any basis of Euclidean n-space. Then the mapping $g(z) = a_n$ where $z = \sum_{i=1}^n a_i z_i$ is obviously a nontrivial 1-form. Note that condition (3) is vacuously satisfied by g. We have immediately

Theorem 1. *Let f be a k-form. Then*

(a) $f(z_1, \ldots, z_{i-1}, z_i + \sum_{j \neq i} a_j z_j, z_{i+1}, \ldots, z_k) = f(z_1, \ldots, z_k)$
  for any scalars a_j and any index i.

(b) $f(z_1, \ldots, z_{i-1}, z_j, z_{i+1}, \ldots, z_{j-1}, z_i, z_{j+1}, \ldots, z_k)$
  $= -f(z_1, \ldots, z_k)$
  for any indices i and j with $1 \leq i < j \leq k$.

(c) $f(z_1, \ldots, z_k) = 0$ *if the vectors $z_1, \ldots, z_k$ are linearly dependent.*

PROOF. To prove (a) select an index $j \neq i$ and a scalar $a_j \neq 0$. Then by (1) and (2)

$f(z_1, \ldots, z_{i-1}, z_i + a_j z_j, z_{i+1}, \ldots, z_k)$

$= f(z_1, \ldots, z_{i-1}, z_i, z_{i+1}, \ldots, z_k) + f(z_1, \ldots, z_{i-1}, a_j z_j, z_{i+1}, \ldots, z_k)$

$= f(z_1, \ldots, z_{i-1}, z_i, z_{i+1}, \ldots, z_k) + a_j f(z_1, \ldots, z_{i-1}, z_j, z_{i+1}, \ldots, z_k)$

But by (3), $f(z_1, \ldots, z_{i-1}, z_j, z_{i+1}, \ldots, z_k) = 0$ because z_j is both

44

the i-th and the j-th argument. Repeated applications of the principle $f(z_1, \ldots, z_{i-1}, z_i + a_j z_j, z_{i+1}, \ldots, z_k) = f(z_1, \ldots, z_k)$ establish (a).

If $i < j$ we obtain from (a) and (3)

$$f(z_1, \ldots, z_{i-1}, z_j, z_{i+1}, \ldots, z_{j-1}, z_i, z_{j+1}, \ldots, z_k) + f(z_1, \ldots, z_k)$$
$$= f(z_1, \ldots, z_{i-1}, z_i + z_j, z_{i+1}, \ldots, z_{j-1}, z_i, z_{j+1}, \ldots, z_k)$$
$$\quad + f(z_1, \ldots, z_{i-1}, z_i + z_j, z_{i+1}, \ldots, z_{j-1}, z_j, z_{j+1}, \ldots, z_k)$$
$$= f(z_1, \ldots, z_{i-1}, z_i + z_j, z_{i+1}, \ldots, z_{j-1}, z_i + z_j, z_{j+1}, \ldots, z_k)$$
$$= 0.$$

This proves (b).

If $z_1, \ldots, z_k$ are linearly dependent, then for some index i and scalars a_j, $z_i + \sum_{j \neq i} a_j z_j = 0$ and

$$f(z_1, \ldots, z_k) = f(z_1, \ldots, z_{i-1}, z_i + \sum_{j \neq i} a_j z_j, z_{i+1}, \ldots, z_k)$$
$$= f(z_1, \ldots, z_{i-1}, 0, z_{i+1}, \ldots, z_k) = 0 f(z_1, \ldots, z_{i-1}, 0, z_{i+1}, \ldots, z_k)$$
$$= 0.$$

This proves (c).

Definition 2. *By a permutation of the integers* $1, \ldots, k$, *we mean a 1–1 mapping* π *of the set* $\{1, \ldots, k\}$ *onto itself. By a transposition we mean a permutation* π *of the integers* $1, \ldots, k$ *for which there exist two integers, i and j, $(i \neq j)$, such that* $\pi(i) = j$, $\pi(j) = i$, *and* $\pi(k) = k$ *for any integer k different from i and j.*

Note that if π is a transposition of $1, \ldots, k$, then π^2 is the identity permutation of $1, \ldots, k$. Permutations will play an important role in our discussion of k-forms.

Theorem 2. *Suppose* $z_1, \ldots, z_k$ *are vectors in Euclidean n-space and c_{ij}, $i, j = 1, \ldots, k$ are scalars. Let f be a k-form. Then*

$$f(w_1, \ldots, w_k) = \sum_\pi c_{1\pi(1)} c_{2\pi(2)} \cdots c_{k\pi(k)} f(z_{\pi(1)}, z_{\pi(2)}, \ldots, z_{\pi(k)})$$

where π runs over all the permutations of $1, \ldots, k$ *and $w_i = \sum_{j=1}^k c_{ij} z_j$, for each $i = 1, \ldots, k$.*

PROOF. We have

$$f(w_1, \ldots, w_k) = f(\sum_{j_1=1}^k c_{1j_1} z_{j_1}, w_2, \ldots, w_k)$$
$$= \sum_{j_1=1}^k c_{1j_1} f(z_{j_1}, w_2, \ldots, w_k)$$
$$= \sum_{j_1=1}^k c_{1j_1} f(z_{j_1}, \sum_{j_2=1}^k c_{2j_2} z_{j_2}, w_3, \ldots, w_k)$$
$$= \sum_{j_1=1}^k c_{1j_1} \sum_{j_2=1}^k c_{2j_2} f(z_{j_1}, z_{j_2}, w_3, \ldots, w_k)$$
$$= \sum_{j_1, j_2} c_{1j_1} c_{2j_2} f(z_{j_1}, z_{j_2}, w_3, \ldots, w_k)$$
$$= \sum_{j_1 j_2 j_3} c_{1j_1} c_{2j_2} c_{3j_3} f(z_{j_1}, z_{j_2}, z_{j_3}, w_4, \ldots, w_k)$$

and repeated applications of this principle show finally that

$$f(w_1, \ldots, w_k) = \sum_{j_1, j_2, \ldots, j_k} c_{1j_1} c_{2j_2} \cdots c_{kj_k} f(z_{j_1}, z_{j_2}, \ldots, z_{j_k}),$$

where the indices $j_1, j_2, \ldots, j_k$ run independently over all integers from 1 to k. However, we can throw out all those terms in which any two of these indices are equal because of part (3) of Definition 1. Hence

$$f(w_1, \ldots, w_k) = \sum_\pi c_{1\pi(1)} c_{2\pi(2)} \cdots c_{k\pi(k)} f(z_{\pi(1)}, z_{\pi(2)}, \ldots, z_{\pi(k)})$$

where π runs over all the permutations of $1, \ldots, k$.

Theorem 3.   *There exists a nontrivial n-form.*

PROOF.   Our construction will proceed in this way; we have already constructed a nontrivial 1-form; we use it to construct a nontrivial 2-form, use this to construct a nontrivial 3-form, and so on until we have a nontrivial n-form. Suppose that f is a nontrivial k-form, $1 \leq k < n$. It suffices to prove that there exists a nontrivial $(k+1)$-form.

Since f is nontrivial, there exist vectors $x_1, \ldots, x_k$ such that $f(x_1, \ldots, x_k) \neq 0$. Clearly $x_1, \ldots, x_k$ are linearly independent; extend these vectors to a basis $\{x_1, \ldots, x_k, x_{k+1}, \ldots, x_n\}$ of Euclidean n-space and let g be the 1-form defined $g(\sum_{i=1}^n c_i x_i) = c_n$. Set

$$
\begin{aligned}
F(z_1, \ldots, z_{k+1}) = &f(z_{k+1}, z_2, \ldots, z_k)g(z_1)\\
&+ f(z_1, z_{k+1}, z_3, \ldots, z_k)g(z_2) + \cdots\\
&+ f(z_1, \ldots, z_{k-1}, z_{k+1})g(z_k)\\
&- f(z_1, \ldots, z_k)g(z_{k+1}).
\end{aligned}
$$

Then $F(x_1, \ldots, x_k, -x_n) = f(x_1, \ldots, x_k) \neq 0$ and it suffices to show that F is a $(k+1)$-form. Now f and g satisfy (1) and (2) of Definition 1 and consequently each of the functions $f(z_{k+1}, z_2, \ldots, z_k)g(z_1), f(z_1, z_{k+1}, z_3, \ldots, z_k)g(z_2), \ldots, f(z_1, \ldots, z_{k-1}, z_{k+1})g(z_k), f(z_1, \ldots, z_k)g(z_{k+1})$ satisfies (1) and (2), and finally F must satisfy (1) and (2) (Problem 3).

We claim that F also satisfies (3). Since f satisfies (3) we have for $z_i = z_j$ and $1 \leq i < j \leq k$,

$$
\begin{aligned}
F(z_1, \ldots, z_{k+1}) = &f(z_{k+1}, z_2, \ldots, z_k)g(z_1)\\
&+ f(z_1, z_{k+1}, z_3, \ldots, z_k)g(z_2) + \cdots\\
&+ f(z_1, \ldots, z_{k-1}, z_{k+1})g(z_k) - f(z_1, \ldots, z_k)g(z_{k+1})\\
= &f(z_1, \ldots, z_{i-1}, z_{k+1}, z_{i+1}, \ldots, z_k)g(z_i)\\
&+ f(z_1, \ldots, z_{j-1}, z_{k+1}, z_{j+1}, \ldots, z_k)g(z_j).
\end{aligned}
$$

But since $z_i = z_j$, we have $f(z_1, \ldots, z_{i-1}, z_{k+1}, z_{i+1}, \ldots, z_k) + f(z_1, \ldots, z_{j-1}, z_{k+1}, z_{j+1}, \ldots, z_k) = 0$ by part (b) of Theorem 1. Hence $F(z_1, \ldots, z_{k+1}) = 0$. On the other hand if $z_i = z_j$ and

$1 \leq i < j = k + 1$, we have

$$F(z_1, \ldots, z_{k+1}) = f(z_1, \ldots, z_{i-1}, z_{k+1}, z_{i+1}, \ldots, z_k)g(z_i)$$
$$- f(z_1, \ldots, z_k)g(z_{k+1}).$$

But since $z_i = z_{k+1}$, it follows that $g(z_i) = g(z_{k+1})$ and

$$f(z_1, \ldots, z_{i-1}, z_{k+1}, z_{i+1}, \ldots, z_k) = f(z_1, \ldots, z_k).$$

Hence $F(z_1, \ldots, z_{k+1}) = 0$ and F satisfies (3). Thus F is a nontrivial $(k+1)$-form and Theorem 4 is proved.

We now show that any permutation on $1, \ldots, k$ is the product of transpositions on $1, \ldots, k$. Here we regard a transposition π as being the product of 1 transposition and we regard the identity mapping as being the product of 0 transpositions.

Lemma 1.   *Let π be a permutation of $1, \ldots, k$. Then there exist transpositions $\sigma_1, \sigma_2, \ldots, \sigma_m$, $m \leq k - 1$, such that $\pi = \sigma_1 \sigma_2 \cdots \sigma_m$.*

PROOF.   The proof is by induction on k. For $k = 1$ the only permutation is the identity mapping and it is the product of 0 transpositions. Now assume that the Lemma is true for permutations of $1, \ldots, k - 1$ where $k \geq 2$, and let π be a permutation of $1, \ldots, k$. Let σ be the permutation for which $\sigma(\pi(k)) = k$, $\sigma(k) = \pi(k)$, and $\sigma(i) = i$ for all integers i different from k and $\pi(k)$. Then $(\sigma\pi)(k) = k$ and σ is either a transposition or the identity mapping. The proof can be completed by considering the permutation of $1, \ldots, k - 1$ induced by $\sigma\pi$ (Problem 4).

Theorem 3 can be used to prove a useful fact about transpositions. Let $\sigma_1, \ldots, \sigma_m$ be transpositions of $1, \ldots, k$ and set $\pi = \sigma_1 \cdots \sigma_m$. Let f be a nontrivial k-form on Euclidean k-space; say $f(x_1, \ldots, x_k) \neq 0$. Then by part (b) of Theorem 1 we have $f(x_{\sigma(1)}, \ldots, x_{\sigma(k)}) = -f(x_1, \ldots, x_k)$ for any transposition σ. Repeated applications of this principle show that $f(x_{\pi(1)}, \ldots, x_{\pi(k)}) = (-1)^m f(x_1, \ldots, x_k)$. Since $f(x_1, \ldots, x_k) \neq -f(x_1, \ldots, x_k)$ it follows that the product of an odd number of transpositions cannot be expressed as the product of an even number of transpositions. Such permutations are called *odd*. Similarly the product of an even number of transpositions cannot be expressed as the product of an odd number of transpositions. These permutations are called *even*. If $\pi = \sigma_1 \cdots \sigma_m$, then $(\sigma_m \cdots \sigma_1)(\sigma_1 \cdots \sigma_m)$ is the identity mapping and $\pi^{-1} = \sigma_m \cdots \sigma_1$. Consequently π and π^{-1} are both even or both odd.

Theorem 4.   *There is one and only one n-form D satisfying $D(e_1, \ldots, e_n) = 1$ (where e_i is the vector in Euclidean n-space with 1 in the i-ith place and 0 in every other place). Furthermore if π is a permutation of $1, \ldots, n$, then $D(e_{\pi(1)}, \ldots, e_{\pi(n)})$ is 1 if π is even and is -1 if π is odd.*

PROOF. Let f be a nontrivial n-form. Then for any vectors $z_1, \ldots, z_n$ with $z_i = \sum_{j=1}^n c_{ij} e_j$, for each $i = 1, \ldots, n$, Theorem 2 gives

$$f(z_1, \ldots, z_n) = \sum_\pi c_{1\pi(1)} \cdots c_{n\pi(n)} f(e_{\pi(1)}, \ldots, e_{\pi(n)})$$

$$= \sum_\pi c_{1\pi(1)} \cdots c_{n\pi(n)} P(\pi) f(e_1, \ldots, e_n)$$

where $P(\pi) = 1$ if π is even and $P(\pi) = -1$ if π is odd. Since f is nontrivial, clearly $f(e_1, \ldots, e_n) \neq 0$. Set $D = f(e_1, \ldots, e_n)^{-1} f$. Then D is an n-form and $D(e_1, \ldots, e_n) = 1$. If D' is another n-form with $D'(e_1, \ldots, e_n) = 1$ then $D - D'$ is also an n-form and $D(e_1, \ldots, e_n) - D'(e_1, \ldots, e_n) = 0$. By the argument just given on f we have $D(z_1, \ldots, z_n) - D'(z_1, \ldots, z_n) = 0$ for any vectors $z_1, \ldots, z_n$ in Euclidean n-space. Of course $D(e_{\pi(1)}, \ldots, e_{\pi(n)}) = P(\pi)$ by the definition of even and odd permutations.

At last we define the determinant of an n by n matrix. Let A be an n by n matrix whose ij-th entry is a_{ij}. We define det A to be $D(r_1, \ldots, r_n)$ where r_i is the i-th row $(a_{i1}, \ldots, a_{in})$. In particular, det $A = \sum_\pi a_{1\pi(1)} \cdots a_{n\pi(n)} P(\pi)$ where π runs over all the permutations of $1, \ldots, n$. But as π runs over all the permutations of $1, \ldots, n$, so also does π^{-1}, and det $A = \sum_\pi a_{1\pi^{-1}(1)} \cdots a_{n\pi^{-1}(n)} P(\pi^{-1}) = \sum_\pi a_{\pi(1)1} \cdots a_{\pi(n)n} P(\pi)$; note that $a_{1\pi^{-1}(1)} \cdots a_{n\pi^{-1}(n)} = a_{\pi(1)1} \cdots a_{\pi(n)n}$, the only difference being in the order of the factors. It follows that det $A = $ det (A^t), where A^t denotes the transpose of A. Hence we can define det A as before by using the columns of A instead of the rows. We conclude with

Theorem 5. *If A and B are n by n matrices then* det $AB = $ (det A)(det B).

PROOF. Let the ij-th entry of A be a_{ij} and let the i-th row of B be r_i. Then by Lecture 2-4 the i-th row of AB is $\sum_{j=1}^n a_{ij} r_j$. Thus

$$\text{det } AB = D\left(\sum_{j=1}^n a_{1j} r_j, \sum_{j=1}^n a_{2j} r_j, \ldots, \sum_{j=1}^n a_{nj} r_j\right)$$

$$= \sum_\pi a_{1\pi(1)} a_{2\pi(2)} \cdots a_{n\pi(n)} D(r_{\pi(1)}, r_{\pi(2)}, \ldots, r_{\pi(n)})$$

by Theorem 2, and

$$\text{det } AB = \sum_\pi a_{1\pi(1)} a_{2\pi(2)} \cdots a_{n\pi(n)} P(\pi) D(r_1, r_2, \ldots, r_n)$$

$$= (\text{det } A)(\text{det } B).$$

If A is nonsingular, then $1 = \text{det } I_n = \text{det } (AA^{-1}) = (\text{det } A)(\text{det } A^{-1})$ and det $A \neq 0$. Indeed, det $A^{-1} = (\text{det } A)^{-1}$. On the other hand, if A is singular, the rows of A are linearly dependent and det $A = 0$.

Problems for Lecture 2—5

1. If $k > n$ prove that there exists no nontrivial k-form. Prove that a linear combination of k-forms is a k-form.

2. Show that for 1 by 1 matrices, det $[c] = c$. Show that for n by n matrices A and scalars c, we have det $(cA) = c^n$ det A.

3. In the proof of Theorem 3 show that F satisfies (1) and (2).

4. Complete the proof of Lemma 1.

5. In the proof of Theorem 4 show that D and $D - D'$ are also n-forms.

6. Let $1 \le k \le n$ and let $z_1, \ldots, z_k$ be vectors in Euclidean n-space, where $z_i = (a_{i1}, a_{i2}, \ldots, a_{in})$. Let t be a mapping of the set $\{1, \ldots, k\}$ into $\{1, \ldots, n\}$ such that $t(1) < t(2) < \cdots < t(k)$. Set $g(z_1, \ldots, z_k) = $ det A where A is the k by k matrix whose i-th row is $(a_{it(1)}, a_{it(2)}, \ldots, a_{it(k)})$. Prove that g is a k-form. Prove that the set of k-forms constitutes a vector space of which k-forms of this type form a basis. (Hint: consider $g(z_1, \ldots, z_k)$ where $a_{ij} = 0$ for every index j different from $t(1), t(2), \ldots, t(k)$.)

7. Let f be a mapping from the set of ordered n-tuples of vectors in Euclidean n-space into the scalars and assume f satisfies
   (1) $f(z_1, \ldots, z_{i-1}, cz_i, z_{i+1}, \ldots, z_n) = cf(z_1, \ldots, z_n)$ for any scalar c and index i.
   (2′) $f(z_1, \ldots, z_{i-1}, z_i + z_j, z_{i+1}, \ldots, z_n) = f(z_1, \ldots, z_n)$ for any indices i, j $(i \ne j)$.
   Prove that f is an n-form. (Hint: If $i < j$ and $z_i = z_j$ show that $f(z_1, \ldots, z_n) = f(z_1, \ldots, z_{i-1}, z_i + z_j, z_{i+1}, \ldots, z_{j-1}, z_j - (z_i + z_j), z_{j+1}, \ldots, z_n) = -f(z_1, \ldots, z_n)$ to establish (3). To prove (2) note that if i is a fixed index and $\{z\} \cup \{z_j\}_{j \ne i}$ is a basis of Euclidean n-space and $z_i = az + \sum_{j \ne i} a_j z_j$, $w_i = bz + \sum_{j \ne i} b_j z_j$, then

$$(a + b)f(z_1, \ldots, z_{i-1}, z, z_{i+1}, \ldots, z_n)$$
$$= f(z_1, \ldots, z_{i-1}, z_i + w_i, z_{i+1}, \ldots, z_n)$$
$$= f(z_1, \ldots, z_{i-1}, z_i, z_{i+1}, \ldots, z_n)$$
$$+ f(z_1, \ldots, z_{i-1}, w_i, z_{i+1}, \ldots, z_n).)$$

8. Let $z_1, \ldots, z_k, k < n$, be linearly independent vectors in Euclidean n-space. Prove that there exists a nontrivial k-form f satisfying $f(z_1, \ldots, z_k) = 0$. (Hint: Extend the given vectors to a basis $\{z_1, \ldots, z_k, z_{k+1}, \ldots, z_n\}$ of Euclidean n-space and consider the argument in Problem 6. Employ this basis instead of the basis $\{e_i\}$.)

9. Let A be an n by n matrix, let B be an m by m matrix, let C be an n by m matrix. By the symbol $\begin{bmatrix} A & C \\ 0 & B \end{bmatrix}$ we mean the $(n + m)$ by $(n + m)$ matrix whose i-th row is the i-th row of A followed by the i-th row of C if $1 \leq i \leq n$, and whose i-th row is the $(i - n)$-th row of B preceded by n 0's if $n + 1 \leq i \leq n + m$.

(a) Prove that $\det \begin{bmatrix} I_n & C \\ 0 & B \end{bmatrix} = \det B$ (Hint: Consider the m-form $\det \begin{bmatrix} I_n & C \\ 0 & B \end{bmatrix}$ on the rows of B.)

(b) Prove that $\det \begin{bmatrix} A & C \\ 0 & B \end{bmatrix} = (\det\ A)(\det\ B)$. (Hint: consider the n-form $\det \begin{bmatrix} A & C \\ 0 & B \end{bmatrix}$ on the columns of A.)

(c) Show that $\det \begin{bmatrix} 1 & C \\ 0 & B \end{bmatrix} = \det B$ where B is m by m and C is 1 by m. Show that $\det \begin{bmatrix} 1 & 0 \\ C & B \end{bmatrix} = \det B$ where B is m by m and C is m by 1.

10. Let A be an n by n matrix whose i-th row is $z_i = (a_{i1}, \ldots, a_{in})$, and let A_{ij} denote the $(n - 1)$ by $(n - 1)$ matrix formed by deleting the i-th row and j-th column of A. Prove that $\det A = \sum_{j=1}^n (-1)^{i+j} a_{ij} \det A_{ij}$ for any index i. (Hint: Show that

$$D(z_1, \ldots, z_n) = \sum_{j=1}^n a_{ij} D(z_1, \ldots, z_{i-1}, e_j, z_{i+1}, \ldots, z_n)$$
$$= \sum_{j=1}^n (-1)^{i-1} a_{ij} D(e_j, z_1, \ldots, z_{i-1}, z_{i+1}, \ldots, z_n)$$
$$= \sum_{j=1}^n (-1)^{i+j-2} a_{ij} \det A_{ij}$$

by switching rows, then columns, and using 9(c).)

11. Prove that in Problem 10 we have $\sum_{j=1}^n (-1)^{i+j} a_{ij} \det A_{kj} = 0$ for $i \neq k$. (Hint: show that $\sum_{j=1}^n (-1)^{i+j} a_{ij} \det A_{kj}$ is the determinant of a matrix B whose i-th and k-th rows coincide.)

12. Construct an analogue of Problem 10 by using columns in place of rows.

13. Let A be a nonsingular n by n matrix. Define A_{ij} as in Problem 10, and define the *adjoint* of A to be the n by n matrix whose ij-th entry is $(-1)^{i+j} \det A_{ji}$.

(a) Use Problems 10 and 11 to prove that $A^{-1} = (\det A)^{-1}(adj\ A)$.

(b) Use Theorem 5 to prove that $\det (adj\ A) = (\det A)^{n-1}$.

(c) Prove that $adj(adj\ A) = (\det A)^{n-2}A$. (Hint: by (a) and (b) we have $A(adj\ A) = (\det A)I_n$ and $[adj\ (adj\ A)](adj\ A) = \det\ (adj\ A)I_n = (\det A)^{n-1}I_n$.) In particular, if $\det A = 1$, then $A = adj(adj\ A)$.

14. Prove that if $A_1, \ldots, A_m$ are square matrices, then the determinant of the direct sum of $A_1, \ldots, A_m$ is $(\det A_1) \cdots (\det A_m)$. (Hint: use induction on m and Problem 9.)

15. Let
$$\begin{cases} a_{11}x_1 + \cdots + a_{1n}x_n = b_1 \\ \quad \cdot \qquad\qquad \cdot \qquad \cdot \\ \quad \cdot \qquad\qquad \cdot \qquad \cdot \\ \quad \cdot \qquad\qquad \cdot \qquad \cdot \\ a_{n1}x_1 + \cdots + a_{nn}x_n = b_n \end{cases}$$
be a system of n equations in n unknowns, and suppose that the matrix
$$A = \begin{bmatrix} a_{11} \cdots a_{1n} \\ \cdot \qquad \cdot \\ \cdot \qquad \cdot \\ a_{n1} \cdots a_{nn} \end{bmatrix}$$
is nonsingular. Let A_i be the matrix formed by replacing the i-th column of A with the vector $(b_1, \ldots, b_n)$. Prove that the one and only solution to this system is $x_i = (\det A)^{-1}(\det A_i)$, $i = 1, \ldots, n$. (Hint: select an index i and observe that 2 rows of the $(n + 1)$ by $(n + 1)$ matrix

$$\begin{bmatrix} a_{i1} \cdots a_{in}, & b_i \\ a_{11} \cdots a_{1n}, & b_1 \\ \cdot \qquad \cdot & \cdot \\ \cdot \qquad \cdot & \cdot \\ \cdot \qquad \cdot & \cdot \\ a_{n1} \cdots a_{nn}, & b_n \end{bmatrix}$$

coincide. Now apply Problem 10 to the top row of this matrix.)

16. Let A^t denote the transpose of an n by n real matrix A. Is it possible that $\det\ (AA^t) = -6$. Explain.

17. Prove that for any scalar c we have
$$\det \begin{bmatrix} c & 1 & 1 & 1 \\ 8 & 2c & -5 & 7 \\ c & 2 & 3 & -1 \\ 0 & c & 2c & -2c \end{bmatrix} = 0.$$

18. Prove that any permutation on $1, \ldots, n$ can be expressed as the product of transpositions that do not map 1 into 1.

Prove that the product of two odd permutations is even, the product of two even permutations is even, and the product of an odd permutation and an even permutation is odd.

19. By an *elementary* matrix we mean a 2 by 2 matrix of the form

$$\begin{bmatrix} a & 0 \\ 0 & 1 \end{bmatrix}, \quad \begin{bmatrix} 1 & 0 \\ 0 & a \end{bmatrix}, \quad \begin{bmatrix} 1 & a \\ 0 & 1 \end{bmatrix}, \quad \begin{bmatrix} 1 & 0 \\ a & 1 \end{bmatrix}, \quad \text{or} \quad \begin{bmatrix} 0 & 1 \\ 1 & 0 \end{bmatrix}$$

where a is a nonzero scalar. Verify the equations

$$\begin{bmatrix} a & 0 \\ 0 & 1 \end{bmatrix} \begin{bmatrix} b & c \\ d & e \end{bmatrix} = \begin{bmatrix} ab & ac \\ d & e \end{bmatrix}, \quad \begin{bmatrix} 1 & 0 \\ 0 & a \end{bmatrix} \begin{bmatrix} b & c \\ d & e \end{bmatrix} = \begin{bmatrix} b & c \\ ad & ae \end{bmatrix},$$

$$\begin{bmatrix} 0 & 1 \\ 1 & 0 \end{bmatrix} \begin{bmatrix} b & c \\ d & e \end{bmatrix} = \begin{bmatrix} d & e \\ b & c \end{bmatrix}, \quad \begin{bmatrix} 1 & a \\ 0 & 1 \end{bmatrix} \begin{bmatrix} b & c \\ d & e \end{bmatrix}$$

$$= \begin{bmatrix} b + ad & c + ae \\ d & e \end{bmatrix}, \quad \begin{bmatrix} 1 & 0 \\ a & 1 \end{bmatrix} \begin{bmatrix} b & c \\ d & e \end{bmatrix} = \begin{bmatrix} b & c \\ ab + d & ac + e \end{bmatrix}.$$

(a) Use Problem 10(d) of Lecture 2-2 to prove that for any 2 by 2 nonsingular matrix A, there exist elementary matrices $E_1, \ldots, E_m$ such that $E_m \cdots E_1 A = I_2$. Hence A^{-1} is the product of elementary matrices, and, likewise, A is the product of elementary matrices.

(b) Generalize this problem to nonsingular n by n matrices A.

20. By a *commutator* we mean a matrix of the form $ABA^{-1}B^{-1}$ where A and B are nonsingular 2 by 2 matrices. Verify the equations

$$\begin{bmatrix} (a+1)^{-1} & 0 \\ 0 & 1 \end{bmatrix} \begin{bmatrix} 1 & 0 \\ 1 & 1 \end{bmatrix} \begin{bmatrix} a+1 & 0 \\ 0 & 1 \end{bmatrix} \begin{bmatrix} 1 & 0 \\ -1 & 1 \end{bmatrix} = \begin{bmatrix} 1 & 0 \\ a & 1 \end{bmatrix} \quad \text{(if } a \neq -1\text{)},$$

$$\begin{bmatrix} 1 & 0 \\ 0 & (a+1)^{-1} \end{bmatrix} \begin{bmatrix} 1 & 1 \\ 0 & 1 \end{bmatrix} \begin{bmatrix} 1 & 0 \\ 0 & a+1 \end{bmatrix} \begin{bmatrix} 1 & -1 \\ 0 & 1 \end{bmatrix} = \begin{bmatrix} 1 & a \\ 0 & 1 \end{bmatrix} \quad \text{(if } a \neq -1\text{)},$$

$$\begin{bmatrix} 1 & 0 \\ 1 & 1 \end{bmatrix} \begin{bmatrix} \frac{1}{2} & 0 \\ 0 & 1 \end{bmatrix} \begin{bmatrix} 1 & 0 \\ -1 & 1 \end{bmatrix} \begin{bmatrix} 2 & 0 \\ 0 & 1 \end{bmatrix} = \begin{bmatrix} 1 & 0 \\ -1 & 1 \end{bmatrix},$$

$$\begin{bmatrix} 1 & 1 \\ 0 & 1 \end{bmatrix} \begin{bmatrix} 1 & 0 \\ 0 & \frac{1}{2} \end{bmatrix} \begin{bmatrix} 1 & -1 \\ 0 & 1 \end{bmatrix} \begin{bmatrix} 1 & 0 \\ 0 & 2 \end{bmatrix} = \begin{bmatrix} 1 & -1 \\ 0 & 1 \end{bmatrix},$$

$$\begin{bmatrix} 1 & -1 \\ 0 & 1 \end{bmatrix} \begin{bmatrix} 1 & 0 \\ 1 & 1 \end{bmatrix} \begin{bmatrix} 0 & 1 \\ 1 & 0 \end{bmatrix} \begin{bmatrix} 1 & 0 \\ -1 & 1 \end{bmatrix} \begin{bmatrix} 0 & 1 \\ 1 & 0 \end{bmatrix} = \begin{bmatrix} 0 & -1 \\ 1 & 0 \end{bmatrix},$$

$$\begin{bmatrix} a & 0 \\ 0 & 1 \end{bmatrix} \begin{bmatrix} 0 & 1 \\ 1 & 0 \end{bmatrix} \begin{bmatrix} a^{-1} & 0 \\ 0 & 1 \end{bmatrix} \begin{bmatrix} 0 & 1 \\ 1 & 0 \end{bmatrix} = \begin{bmatrix} a & 0 \\ 0 & a^{-1} \end{bmatrix} \quad \text{(if } a \neq 0\text{)}.$$

(a) Prove that any 2 by 2 matrix A satisfying det $A = 1$ is the product of commutators.

(b) Generalize this problem to n by n matrices A satisfying det $A = 1$.

21. Let ϕ be a mapping of the set of nonsingular n by n matrices into nonzero scalars such that $\phi(AB) = \phi(A)\phi(B)$ for matrices A and B. Prove that $\phi(A) = \phi(B)$ if det $A = $ det B. (Hint: $\phi(ABA^{-1}B^{-1}) = \phi(A)\phi(A^{-1})\phi(B)\phi(B^{-1}) = \phi(AA^{-1}BB^{-1}) = \phi(I_n) = \phi(I_n)^2 = 1$. Use Problem 20 to show that if det $A = $ det B, then AB^{-1} is the product of commutators.)

Lecture 2–6

Operators on a Vector Space.   In this lecture we shall define a certain type of function mapping a vector space V into itself. Abandoning our previous notation concerning functions, we shall find it convenient to write the function on the right and the argument on the left; e.g., $(x)T$ will denote the image of the vector x under the function T.

Definition 1.   *A mapping T of a vector space V into V is a (linear) operator on V if it satisfies*

(1) $(z_1 + z_2)T = z_1 T + z_2 T$ *for any* $z_1, z_2 \in V$,

(2) $(az)T = a(zT)$ *for any* $z \in V$ *and any scalar a.*

Note that (1) and (2) can both be expressed by the equation $(a_1 z_1 + a_2 z_2)T = a_1(z_1 T) + a_2(z_2 T)$ for any $z_1, z_2 \in V$ and any scalars a_1, a_2 (Problem 1). If r is a fixed scalar, then the mapping T defined by the equation $zT = rz$ is easily shown to be an operator on V. Note that $(z_1 + z_2)T = r(z_1 + z_2) = rz_1 + rz_2 = z_1 T + z_2 T$ and $(az)T = raz = a(rz) = a(zT)$. The operator defined in this way by means of a scalar r is called the *scalar operator r*. (The operator r and the scalar r will always be distinguishable from the context.) In particular, the operator 1 is the identity mapping of V onto V, and the operator 0 carries every vector in V to the vector 0.

By the *null space* of an operator T on V we mean the set of all vectors z satisfying $zT = 0$. By the null space of a family of operators M, we mean the set of all vectors z satisfying $zT = 0$ for each $T \in M$. We also say that M *annihilates* a set of vectors Z if Z is a subset of the null space of M. We see immediately that the null space of T is a subspace of V.

Theorem 1.   *Let T be an operator on V with null space N. Then N and VT are subspaces of V.*

Proof.   Since $(0)T = (0 + 0)T = (0)T + (0)T$ it follows that $(0)T = 0$, and N is nonvoid. If $z_1, z_2 \in N$ and a is a scalar, then $(z_1 + z_2)T = z_1 T + z_2 T = 0 + 0 = 0$, and $(az_1)T = a(z_1 T) = a0 = 0$. This proves that N is a subspace of V.

If $z_1, z_2 \in V$ and a is a scalar, then $(z_1 + z_2)T = z_1 T + z_2 T$ and $a(z_1 T) = (az_1)T$. Since VT is nonvoid, this proves that VT is a subspace of V.

54

The next result provides a wealth of examples of operators on V.

Theorem 2. *Let $\{z_1, \ldots, z_n\}$ be an ordered basis of V and let $w_1, \ldots, w_n$ be n vectors in V. Then there exists one and only one operator T on V satisfying $z_i T = w_i$, for each $i = 1, \ldots, n$.*

PROOF. We define the mapping T as follows; for $z = \sum_i a_i z_i$ set $zT = \sum_i a_i w_i$. That T is an operator on V follows from the equations

$$\left(\sum_i a_i z_i + \sum_i b_i z_i\right) T = \left(\sum_i (a_i + b_i) z_i\right) T = \sum_i (a_i + b_i) w_i$$
$$= \sum_i a_i w_i + \sum_i b_i w_i = \left(\sum_i a_i z_i\right) T + \left(\sum_i b_i z_i\right) T$$

and

$$\left(a\sum_i a_i z_i\right) T = \sum_i (aa_i) w_i = a\sum_i a_i w_i = a\left(\sum_i a_i z_i\right) T.$$

In particular, we have $z_j T = w_j$ for each $j = 1, \ldots, n$.

Now if S is another operator (on V) satisfying $z_j S = w_j$ for each $j = 1, \ldots, n$, we have $\left(\sum_i a_i z_i\right) T = \sum_i a_i w_i = \left(\sum_i a_i z_i\right) S$ and S and T coincide. This concludes the proof.

If $\{z_1, \ldots, z_m\}$ is a linearly independent set of vectors in V and if $w_1, \ldots, w_m$ are m vectors in V, then there exists an operator T on V satisfying $z_i T = w_i$ for each i. To see this extend $\{z_1, \ldots, z_m\}$ to a basis of V. Of course, the operator T will not be unique if $\{z_1, \ldots, z_m\}$ is not a basis of V (Problem 2).

We say that two operators S and T on V are equal ($S = T$) if S and T are the same function. If T_1 and T_2 are operators on V we define $T_1 + T_2$ as follows: $z(T_1 + T_2) = zT_1 + zT_2$. That $T_1 + T_2$ is an operator on V follows from

$$(az + bw)(T_1 + T_2) = (az + bw) T_1 + (az + bw) T_2$$
$$= a(zT_1) + b(wT_1) + a(zT_2) + b(wT_2)$$
$$= a[zT_1 + zT_2] + b[wT_1 + wT_2]$$
$$= a[z(T_1 + T_2)] + b[w(T_1 + T_2)]$$

for any $z, w \in V$ and any scalars a, b. We define the operator $T_1 T_2$ as follows; $z(T_1 T_2) = (zT_1) T_2$. That $T_1 T_2$ is an operator follows from

$$(az + bw)(T_1 T_2) = [(az + bw) T_1] T_2 = (a(zT_1) + b(wT_1)) T_2$$
$$= a(zT_1) T_2 + b(wT_1) T_2$$
$$= a(zT_1 T_2) + b(wT_1 T_2)$$

for any $z, w \in V$ and any scalars a, b. By induction we can define (Problem 3) the product $T_1 \cdots T_m$ if $T_1, \ldots, T_m$ are operators. (Note that in $z(T_1 \cdots T_m)$, the operators are applied from left to right.) If a is a scalar and T is an operator, we define the operator

aT as follows; $z(aT) = a(zT)$. That aT is an operator follows from

$$(bz + cw)(aT) = a(bz + cw)T = (ab)(zT) + (ac)(wT)$$
$$= b(z(aT)) + c(w(aT)).$$

The next result parallels Theorem 1 of Lecture 2-4.

Theorem 3.   *For all operators R, S, T on V and all scalars a, b we have*

(1) $(R + S) + T = R + (S + T)$

(2) $T + 0 = 0$

(3)   *For any T there is a unique operator $-T$ for which $T + (-T) = (-T) + T = 0$.*

(4) $S + T = T + S$

(5) $1T = T1 = T$

(6) $(RS)T = R(ST)$

(7) $R(S + T) = RS + RT$

(8) $(R + S)T = RT + ST$

(9) $(aS)T = a(ST)$

(10) $a(S + T) = aS + aT$

(11) $(a + b)T = aT + bT$

These properties are verified by routine arguments (Problem 4). We shall only sketch the more difficult arguments. For any vector $z \in V$ we have

$$z[(RS)T] = [z(RS)]T = [(zR)S]T = (zR)(ST) = z[R(ST)].$$

This proves (6). In (3) we need only set $-T = (-1)T$; then for any $z \in V$ we have $z(T + (-T)) = zT + (-1)(zT) = zT - zT = 0$ and $T + (-T) = 0$. If $T + S = 0$ also, then $z(S + T) = 0 = zT + zS = zT + z(-T)$ and $zS = z(-T)$. This establishes the uniqueness of $-T$. Also

$$z[(R + S)T] = [z(R + S)]T = (zR + zS)T = (zR)T$$
$$+ (zS)T = z(RT) + z(ST)$$

for any $z \in V$. This establishes (8).

Let $\{z_1, \ldots, z_n\}$ and $\{w_1, \ldots, w_n\}$ be ordered bases of a vector space V. Suppose a_{ij} are the scalars such that $w_i = \sum_{j=1}^{n} a_{ij} z_j$ for each index $i = 1, \ldots, n$. Let A be the n by n matrix whose ij-th entry is a_{ij}. We call A the *change of basis* matrix from $\{z_1, \ldots, z_n\}$ to $\{w_1, \ldots, w_n\}$. We claim that A is nonsingular; for if x_i is the i-th row $(a_{i1}, a_{i2}, \ldots, a_{in})$ of A and if $c_1, c_2, \ldots, c_n$ are scalars such that $\sum_{i=1}^{n} c_i x_i = (0, 0, \ldots, 0)$, it follows that $\sum_{i=1}^{n} c_i a_{ij} = 0$ for each $j = 1, \ldots, n$, and

$$0 = \sum_{j=1}^{n} \left(\sum_{i=1}^{n} c_i a_{ij} z_j\right) = \sum_{i=1}^{n} c_i \left(\sum_{j=1}^{n} a_{ij} z_j\right) = \sum_{i=1}^{n} c_i w_i,$$

and $c_i = 0$ for each $i = 1, \ldots, n$.

Let T be an operator on V and let $\{z_1, \ldots, z_n\}$ be an ordered basis of V. By the *matrix of T relative to the ordered basis* $\{z_1, \ldots, z_n\}$ we mean the matrix A whose ij-th entry is a_{ij}, where $z_iT = \sum_{j=1}^{n} a_{ij}z_j$ for each $i = 1, \ldots, n$. The matrix A is uniquely determined in this way by T and $\{z_1, \ldots, z_n\}$. Likewise A and $\{z_1, \ldots, z_n\}$ uniquely determine T (Problem 5). Note that if $\{z_1T, \ldots, z_nT\}$ is a basis of V, then A is also the change of basis matrix from $\{z_1, \ldots, z_n\}$ to $\{z_1T, \ldots, z_nT\}$.

Theorem 4. *Let S, T be operators on V, let $\{z_1, \ldots, z_n\}$ be an ordered basis of V and let A, B be the matrices of S, T, respectively, relative to $\{z_1, \ldots, z_n\}$. Then relative to $\{z_1, \ldots, z_n\}$*
(1)   *the matrix of $S + T$ is $A + B$,*
(2)   *the matrix of ST is AB,*
(3)   *the matrix of rS is rA for any scalar r.*

PROOF.   Let a_{ij} be the ij-th entry of A and b_{ij} the ij-th entry of B. Then

$$z_i(S + T) = z_iS + z_iT = \sum_{j=1}^{n} a_{ij}z_j + \sum_{j=1}^{n} b_{ij}z_j$$
$$= \sum_{j=1}^{n} (a_{ij} + b_{ij})z_j.$$

Hence $a_{ij} + b_{ij}$ is the ij-th entry of the matrix of $S + T$ relative to $\{z_1, \ldots, z_n\}$. This proves (1).

Also,

$$z_i(ST) = (z_iS)T = \left(\sum_{k=1}^{n} a_{ik}z_k\right)T = \sum_{k=1}^{n} a_{ik}(z_kT)$$
$$= \sum_{k=1}^{n} a_{ik}\left(\sum_{j=1}^{n} b_{kj}z_j\right) = \sum_{j=1}^{n} \sum_{k=1}^{n} (a_{ik}b_{kj})z_j.$$

Hence the ij-th entry of the matrix of ST relative to $\{z_1, \ldots, z_n\}$ is $\sum_{k=1}^{n} a_{ik}b_{kj}$. This proves (2).

Finally, $z_i(rS) = r(z_iS) = r(\sum_{j=1}^{n} a_{ij}z_j) = \sum_{j=1}^{n} ra_{ij}z_j$, and the ij-th entry of the matrix of rS relative to $\{z_1, \ldots, z_n\}$ is ra_{ij}. This proves (3).

Theorem 5. *Let T be an operator on V, let $\{z_1, \ldots, z_n\}$ and $\{w_1, \ldots, w_n\}$ be ordered bases of V, let A, B be the respective matrices of T relative to $\{z_1, \ldots, z_n\}$ and $\{w_1, \ldots, w_n\}$. Then A and B are similar. More precisely, $B = CAC^{-1}$ where C is the change of basis matrix from $\{z_1, \ldots, z_n\}$ to $\{w_1, \ldots, w_n\}$.*

PROOF.   Say $w_i = \sum_{j=1}^{n} c_{ij}z_j$ for each $i = 1, \ldots, n$; then c_{ij} is the ij-th entry of C. Let S be the operator whose matrix relative to $\{z_1, \ldots, z_n\}$ is B, and let R be the operator whose matrix relative to $\{z_1, \ldots, z_n\}$ is C. Then $z_iR = \sum_{j=1}^{n} c_{ij}z_j = w_i$ for each $i = 1, \ldots, n$, and $z_iRT = w_iT = \sum_{j=1}^{n} b_{ij}w_j$, for each $i = 1, \ldots, n$. On the other hand $z_iSR = (\sum_{j=1}^{n} b_{ij}z_j)R = \sum_{j=1}^{n} b_{ij}(z_jR) = \sum_{j=1}^{n} b_{ij}w_j$. Clearly $RT = SR$ by Theorem 2, and RT and SR have the same matrix relative to $\{z_1, \ldots, z_n\}$. By Theorem 4 we obtain $CA = BC$. Hence $B = (BC)C^{-1} = CAC^{-1}$ and the proof is complete.

Thus any two matrices associated with the operator T (relative to some ordered bases) must be similar. Now suppose that A is the matrix of T relative to an ordered basis $\{z_1, \ldots, z_n\}$, and let C be nonsingular. Let c_{ij} be the ij-th entry of C and set $w_i = \sum_{j=1}^{n} c_{ij} z_j$. Then $\{w_1, \ldots, w_n\}$ is an ordered basis of V, because $0 = \sum_{i=1}^{n} b_i(\sum_{j=1}^{n} c_{ij} z_j) = \sum_{j=1}^{n}(\sum_{i=1}^{n} b_i c_{ij}) z_j$ implies $\sum_{i=1}^{n} b_i c_{ij} = 0$ for each $j = 1, \ldots, n$, and $b_i = 0$ for each $i = 1, \ldots, n$. Furthermore, C is the change of basis matrix from $\{z_1, \ldots, z_n\}$ to $\{w_1, \ldots, w_n\}$ and by Theorem 5, CAC^{-1} is the matrix of T relative to $\{w_1, \ldots, w_n\}$. Thus any matrix similar to A is associated with T relative to an appropriate ordered basis.

By the *determinant* of the operator T we mean the determinant of any matrix A associated with T (relative to some ordered basis). Now det T is well defined; for if B is another matrix associated with T, there exists a nonsingular matrix C such that $B = CAC^{-1}$ and

$$\text{det } B = \text{det } (CAC^{-1}) = (\text{det } C)(\text{det } A)(\text{det } C^{-1})$$
$$= (\text{det } C)(\text{det } C^{-1})(\text{det } A) = (\text{det } I_n)(\text{det } A) = \text{det } A.$$

For any operator T on V we define T^2 to be the operator TT, T^3 to be the operator TT^2, and in general, T^m to be TT^{m-1}. In particular, $T^p T^q = T^{p+q}$ (Problem 6). For consistency, we let T^0 denote the scalar operator 1. If $p(x) = a_0 + a_1 x + a_2 x^2 + \cdots + a_m x^m$ is a polynomial with scalar coefficients a_i, we define $p(T)$ to be $a_0 + a_1 T + a_2 T^2 + \cdots + a_m T^m$. Then if A is the matrix of T relative to the ordered basis $\{z_1, \ldots, z_n\}$, we have that $p(A)$ is the matrix of $p(T)$ relative to $\{z_1, \ldots, z_n\}$. We say that the polynomial p *annuls* T if $p(T) = 0$. (Note that p annuls T iff p annuls A.) If p annuls T and q is another polynomial, then pq annuls T (Problem 16). If S and T are operators on V we say that T commutes with S if $ST = TS$. If p and q are polynomials and S commutes with T, then $p(S)$ commutes with $q(T)$ (Problem 7). As with matrices, there do exist operators (on V) that do not commute (Problem 8).

Let U be a subspace of V and let T be an operator on V. We say that U is *invariant under* T if $UT \subset U$, where UT denotes the set $\{uT : u \in U\}$. If U is invariant under T, then the mapping T from U into U is an operator on the space U; this operator on U implemented by T is called the *contraction* of T to U. (Note that if U is a subspace of V annihilated by T, then U is invariant under T and the contraction of T to U is the operator 0.) Suppose A is the matrix of the contraction of T to U relative to an ordered basis of U. Then we can construct an ordered basis of V relative to which the matrix of T has the form $\begin{bmatrix} B & C \\ 0 & A \end{bmatrix}$ for some matrix C and some square matrix B (Problem 9).

Let M be a family of operators on V and let T be an operator on V. By the sets MT, TM, and $T + M$, we mean, respectively, $\{ST: S \in M\}$, $\{TS: S \in M\}$, and $\{T + S: S \in M\}$. For example, the equation $MT = TM$ would mean that MT and TM are the same family of operators. The subspace U of V is said to be invariant under M if $UM \subset U$, where UM denotes the set $\{uT: u \in U, T \in M\}$, and U is said to be annihilated by M if $UM = (0)$ (as we mentioned before). If U is invariant under M, we call the family of contractions of operators in M to U the contraction of M to U. If M and N are families of operators on V, then MN denotes the set $\{ST: S \in M, T \in N\}$.

The family of all operators on the vector space V forms a vector space. By considering the matrices of these operators relative to a certain fixed ordered basis, we see from Theorem 4 and from Lecture 2-4 that the dimension of this vector space is $(\dim V)^2$ (Problem 10).

Let T be an operator on a real vector space and let $V + iV$ be the complexification of V. Define the mapping T' of $V + iV$ into $V + iV$ as follows; $(x + iy) T' = xT + iyT$. One can easily show that T' is an operator on the complex vector space $V + iV$ (Problem 11). If $\{z_1, \ldots, z_n\}$ is an ordered basis of V, then $\{z_1, \ldots, z_n\}$ is also an ordered basis of $V + iV$ and the matrix of T' relative to $\{z_1, \ldots, z_n\}$ is obviously the same as the matrix of T relative to $\{z_1, \ldots, z_n\}$. This matrix, of course, has real entries.

Now suppose S is an operator on the complex vector space $V + iV$. Define the mappings S_r and S_i of V into V as follows; $xS_r = y$, $xS_i = z$ where $xS = y + iz$ and $x, y, z \in V$. One can easily show that S_r and S_i are operators on the real vector space V (Problem 11). Let $\{z_1, \ldots, z_n\}$ be an ordered basis of V; let A and B be the respective matrices of S_r and S_i relative to this ordered basis. Then $\{z_1, \ldots, z_n\}$ is also an ordered basis of $V + iV$ and, as in the preceding paragraph, let S_r' and S_i' denote the respective operators on $V + iV$ with matrices A and B relative to $\{z_1, \ldots, z_n\}$. Then for $x \in V$ we have $xS = y + iz$ for some $y, z \in V$ and $xS = xS_r + ixS_i = xS_r' + ixS_i' = x(S_r' + iS_i')$. Thus S coincides with the operator $S_r' + iS_i'$ on V and, hence, on $V + iV$. We call S_r the *real part* of S, and S_i, the *imaginary part* of S. Since $S = S_r' + iS_i'$ we have that $A + iB$ is the matrix of S relative to $\{z_1, \ldots, z_n\}$. Now let T and T' be defined as in the preceding paragraph and let C be the matrix of T relative to $\{z_1, \ldots, z_n\}$. If T' commutes with S, then $C(A + iB) = CA + iCB = AC + iBC = (A + iB)C$ and $CA = AC$, $CB = BC$. Hence T commutes with the real and imaginary parts of S on V. On the other hand if T commutes with the real and imaginary parts of S, we have $CA = AC$, $BC = CB$, and $C(A + iB) = CA + iCB = AC + iBC = (A + iB)C$, and T' must commute with S on $V + iV$.

Now suppose that p is a polynomial with real coefficients and T and T' are given as before. Then T is the real part of T', 0 is the imaginary part of T', $p(T)$ is the real part of $p(T')$, and 0 is the imaginary part of $p(T')$ (Problem 13). Furthermore, p annuls T iff p annuls T' (Problem 14); this can be established by comparing matrices.

Problems for Lecture 2—6

1. Show that a mapping T of the vector space V into V is an operator iff $(a_1 z_1 + a_2 z_2)T = a_1(z_1 T) + a_2(z_2 T)$ for any scalars a_1, a_2 and any vectors z_1, z_2.

2. Let $\{z_1, \ldots, z_m\}$ be a linearly independent set of vectors on a space V with $m < \dim V$, and let $w_1, \ldots, w_m$ be m vectors in V. Prove that there exists more than one operator T satisfying $z_i T = w_i$ for each $i = 1, \ldots, m$.

3. Use induction on m to define the operator $T_1 \cdots T_m$ where the T_i are operators on V.

4. Prove all parts of Theorem 3.

5. Let A be the matrix of an operator T on a vector space V relative to the ordered basis $\{z_1, \ldots, z_n\}$. Prove that A and $\{z_1, \ldots, z_n\}$ determine T. Do T and A determine $\{z_1, \ldots, z_n\}$? Explain.

6. Given an operator T on V, use induction on m to define T^m and prove that $T^p T^q = T^{p+q}$ for any integers p, $q > 0$.

7. Prove that if p and q are polynomials and S and T are commuting operators on V, then $p(S)$ and $q(T)$ commute.

8. Construct two noncommuting operators on a vector space.

9. Let U be a subspace of V invariant under the operator T and let A be a matrix associated with the contraction of T to U. Prove that there exists a square matrix B and a matrix C such that $\begin{bmatrix} B & C \\ 0 & A \end{bmatrix}$ is associated with the operator T on V.

   (Hint: construct an ordered basis of V the last m members of which form an appropriate ordered basis of U.)

10. Prove that the operators on a vector space V form a vector space of dimension $(\dim V)^2$.

11. Let T be an operator on the real vector space V and let T' be the mapping already defined on the complexification $V + iV$ of V. Prove that T' is an operator on the complex vector space $V + iV$. Let S be an operator on $V + iV$ and let S_r and S_i be the mappings on V defined before. Prove that S_r and S_i are operators on the real vector space V.

12. In Problem 11 prove without using matrices that T commutes with S_r and S_i iff T' commutes with S.

13. In Problem 11 prove that T is the real part of T' and 0 is the imaginary part of T'. If p is a polynomial with real coefficients prove that $p(T)$ is the real part of $p(T')$ and 0 is the imaginary part of $p(T')$.

14. In Problem 13 prove that p annuls T iff p annuls T'.

15. Show that the matrix of the scalar operator r on an n-dimensional vector space V is rI_n relative to any ordered basis of V.

16. Let p, q be polynomials and let T be an operator on V. Prove in detail that $(pq)(T) = p(T)q(T)$ and $(p + q)(T) = p(T) + q(T)$. Prove that $(cp)(T) = cp(T)$ for any scalar c.

17. If U is a subspace invariant under the operator T, prove that U is invariant under $p(T)$ for any polynomial p.

18. Let T be an operator on $V = U_1 \oplus \cdots \oplus U_m$ where each subspace U_i is invariant under T. Suppose the contraction of T to U_i is associated with the matrix A_i (relative to some ordered basis of U_i). Prove that the operator T on V is associated with the direct sum $A_1 \oplus \cdots \oplus A_m$ (relative to some ordered basis of V).

Part 3 OPERATORS ON VECTOR SPACES

Lecture 3–1

Introduction. In Part 2 we introduced matrices, determinants, and operators on vector spaces. In the present part we relate the notions of matrix, operator, and basis of a vector space. In Lecture 3-5 we define the characteristic polynomial of an operator, and develop the properties of the characteristic polynomial, including the Cayley-Hamilton equation (without employing determinants). We then use determinants to compute the characteristic polynomials of concrete matrices and operators. In Lecture 3-6 we develop the Jordan form of an operator and prove the uniqueness of the Jordan form by employing the dimension of the range spaces of certain operators. In the list of problems for Lecture 3-5 we show how the characteristic polynomial can be developed by use of real scalars (rather than complex scalars). In the list of problems for Lecture 3-6 we show how the Jordan form of a (reasonable) matrix or operator can be computed. The principal idea employed in both Lectures 3-5 and 3-6 is the dimension of a vector space.

Lectures 3-2, 3-3, and 3-4 exist primarily to prepare us for Lectures 3-5, 3-6, and later parts. In these lectures we study eigenvalues and eigenvectors of operators, similar operators, operators induced on quotient spaces, operators induced on subspaces, and the range and null space of an operator. We also introduce projection operators, which will assume considerable importance in Parts 4 and 5. In Lecture 3-4 we show that pairwise commuting diagonable operators can be "simultaneously diagonalized." We also show that pairwise commuting operators can be "simultaneously associated with triangular matrices." In Lecture 3-2 we discuss singular and nonsingular operators, and prove that an operator commuting with every operator must be a scalar operator.

$\mathcal{L}$ecture 3–2

The Range and Null Space of an Operator. In Lecture 2-6 we defined the range of the operator T on V to be the set VT, and the null space of T to be the set of all vectors annihilated by T. We proved that the range and null space of T are both subspaces of V. In particular, the range of the operator 1 is V and the null space of 1 is (0). The range of the operator 0 is (0) and the null space of 0 is V.

We say that an operator P on V is a *projection* if $P^2 = P$; equivalently, P is a projection iff $z \in VP$ implies $zP = z$. If P is a projection note that $V(1 - P)$ is the null space of P. To see this observe that $V(1 - P)P = V(P - P^2) = (0)$; on the other hand, if $zP = 0$, then $z = z - zP = z(1 - P) \in V(1 - P)$. Furthermore, $1 - P$ is also a projection (because $(1 - P)^2 = 1 - P - P + P^2 = 1 - P$) with null space VP. Also $(VP) \cap V(1 - P) = (0)$; for if $z \in (VP) \cap V(1 - P)$, then $zP = 0 = z(1 - P)$ and $z = zP + z(1 - P) = 0$. Thus the range and null space of a projection are complementary subspaces of V.

Examples of projections are easily found. Let U and W be complementary subspaces of V. Set $zP = w$ where $z = w + u$, $w \in W$, $u \in U$. To show that P is an operator observe that if w_1, $w_2 \in W$, u_1, $u_2 \in U$, then $(w_1 + u_1 + w_2 + u_2)P = w_1 + w_2 = (w_1 + u_1)P + (w_2 + u_2)P$ and $(cw_1 + cu_1)P = cw_1 = c(w_1 + u_1)P$. Now if $z \in V$, then $zP \in W$, $zP^2 = (zP)P = zP$ and $P^2 = P$. Thus P, so defined, is a projection with range W and null space U.

Projection operators will play a considerable role in the remainder of our work. We relate the null space and range of any operator in

Theorem 1. *Let T be a nonzero operator on an n-dimensional vector space V and let T have null space U. Then $\dim VT + \dim U = n$. Furthermore there exists an operator S (on V) satisfying $\dim VS = \dim VT$ and such that ST is a projection with range VT and $1 - TS$ is a projection with range U.*

PROOF. Let W be a subspace of V complementary to U. Let m denote $\dim U$ and select a basis $\{z_1, \ldots, z_m\}$ of U and a basis $\{z_{m+1}, \ldots, z_n\}$ of W. (We do not exclude the possibility that $U = (0)$. In this event $m = 0$ and $\{z_1, \ldots, z_m\}$ is the void set.)

66

Then $\{z_1, \ldots, z_m, \ldots, z_n\}$ is a basis of V. For $z = \sum_i c_i z_i$ we have $zT = \sum_i c_i(z_i T) = \sum_{i=m+1}^n c_i(z_i T)$. Thus the vectors $z_{m+1}T, \ldots, z_n T$ span VT. Furthermore, these vectors are linearly independent; for if $\sum_{i=m+1}^n c_i(z_i T) = 0$, then $(\sum_{i=m+1}^n c_i z_i) T = 0$, $\sum_{i=m+1}^n c_i z_i \in U \cap W$, $\sum_{i=m+1}^n c_i z_i = 0$, and $c_i = 0$ for each $i = m+1, \ldots, n$. Thus VT has a basis composed of $n - m$ vectors, and dim $VT = n - m = n - \dim U$.

Select a subspace U_1 complementary to VT. The reader can easily show (Problem 1) that there exists an operator S on V annihilating U_1 such that $(z_i T)S = z_i$ for each $i = m+1, \ldots, n$. By essentially the same argument employed to prove dim $VT = n - m$ it follows that dim $VS = n - m = \dim VT$ (Problem 2).

Finally, for each $i = m+1, \ldots, n$, we have $z_i(TS) = (z_i T)S = z_i$. For $z = \sum_i c_i z_i$, we have

$$z(TS)^2 = (\textstyle\sum_{i=1}^n c_i z_i T)(STS)$$
$$= (\textstyle\sum_{i=m+1}^n c_i z_i TS)(TS) = (\textstyle\sum_{i=1}^n c_i z_i) TS = zTS.$$

Hence TS is a projection with null space U (Problem 3), and $1 - TS$ is a projection with range U. The reader can easily show in a similar way that ST is a projection with range VT (Problem 4).

Theorem 2. *Let T be an operator on V. Then the following are equivalent.*
(1) *The null space of T is (0).*
(2) *$VT = V$.*
In the event (1) *and* (2) *hold there is a unique operator S for which $ST = TS = 1$.*

PROOF. To prove (1) $\Leftrightarrow$ (2) recall that dim $VT + \dim U = \dim V$ by Theorem 1. Thus if dim $U = 0$, then dim $VT = \dim V$ and $VT = V$. On the other hand, if dim $VT = \dim V$, then dim $U = 0$ and $U = (0)$.

Now assume (1) and (2) hold. By Theorem 1 there exists an operator S such that ST is a projection with range $VT = V$ and $1 - TS$ is a projection whose range is the null space of T. It follows that $1 - TS = 0$ and $ST = 1$. Hence $ST = TS = 1$. To prove that S is unique let R be an operator such that $RT = TR = 1$. Then $S = S(TR) = (ST)R = R$.

If an operator T satisfies (1) and (2) in Theorem 2 we say that T is *nonsingular* (or *invertible*). The operator S is called the *inverse* of T and is often denoted T^{-1}. Of course T^{-1} is also nonsingular and T is the inverse of T^{-1}.

If S and T are operators on V such that $ST = 1$, then $V(ST) = V$, $VT = V$ and T is nonsingular. Also the null space of ST and of S is (0), and S is nonsingular. Furthermore $S = S(TT^{-1}) = (ST)T^{-1} = T^{-1}$ and $T = (S^{-1}S)T = S^{-1}(ST) = S^{-1}$.

Theorem 3.   *Let S and T be operators on V and let U be the null space of T.   Then*
(1)   *If $ST = TS$, then $(VT)S \subset VT$ and $US \subset U$.*
(2)   *If T is a projection, then $ST = TS$ iff $(VT)S \subset VT$ and $US \subset U$.*

PROOF.   To prove (1) suppose that $ST = TS$.   Then $(VT)S = V(TS) = V(ST) = (VS)T \subset VT$.   If $z \in U$, then $(zS)T = (zT)S = 0S = 0$ and $zS \in U$.   Thus $US \subset U$ and (1) is proved.

To prove (2) let T be a projection.   Suppose $(VT)S \subset VT$ and $US \subset U$.   Then if $x \in VT, y \in V(1 - T)$, we have $(x + y)(ST) = (xS)T + (yS)T = xS$ because $xS \in VT$ and $yS \in V(1 - T)$.   Also $(x + y)(TS) = (xT)S + (yT)S = xS$ and $(x + y)(ST) = (x + y)(TS)$.   Thus $ST = TS$ and (2) is proved.

Theorem 4.   *Let S and T be operators on an n-dimensional vector space V, let U be the null space of S, let W be the null space of T, and let X be the null space of ST.   Then*
(1) $\dim X \leq \dim U + \dim W$.   *Furthermore, equality holds iff $W \subset VS$.*
(2) $\dim U \leq \dim X$ *and* $\dim W \leq \dim X$.

PROOF.   Let $\{z_1, \ldots, z_m\}$ be a basis of a subspace Z satisfying $VS = Z \oplus (VS \cap W)$.   By an argument employed in the proof of Theorem 1 one can show that the vectors $z_1 T, \ldots, z_m T$ form a basis of $V(ST)$.   (See Problem 5.)   Then

$$m = \dim VS - \dim (VS \cap W) = n - \dim U - \dim (VS \cap W)$$

and $m = \dim V(ST) = n - \dim X$.   Thus

$$\dim X = \dim U + \dim (VS \cap W) \leq \dim U + \dim W.$$

Furthermore, $\dim X = \dim U + \dim W$ iff $\dim W = \dim (VS \cap W)$.   But $\dim W = \dim (VS \cap W)$ iff $W \subset VS$.   This establishes (1).

To prove (2) observe that $V(ST) = (VS)T \subset VT$ and $\dim V(ST) \leq \dim VT$.   Hence $\dim X = n - \dim V(ST) \geq n - \dim VT = \dim W$.   If $zS = 0$ then $z(ST) = 0$, and $U \subset X$.   Finally $\dim U \leq \dim X$.

It follows from Theorem 4 that if $T_1, \ldots, T_m$ are operators on V where U_i is the null space of T_i and U is the null space of $T_1 \cdots T_m$, then $\sum_i \dim U_i \geq \dim U$.   In particular, if $T_1 \cdots T_m = 0$, then $\sum_i \dim U_i \geq \dim V$.

We now give a partial converse to part (2) of Theorem 3.

Theorem 5.   *Let T be a nonzero operator on V, with null space U, and that commutes with every projection P satisfying $(VT)P \subset VT$ and $UP \subset U$.   Then T is a scalar multiple of a projection.*

PROOF.   Let P be a projection with range $VT \cap U$.   Then $(VT)P = VT \cap U \subset VT$ and $UP = VT \cap U \subset U$.   By hypothesis

$PT = TP$ and $VT \cap U = [VT \cap U]P \subset (VTP) \cap UP \subset VPT = [VT \cap U]T = (0)$. Hence $VT \cap U = (0)$. Let Q be a projection with null space $VT + U$. Then $(VT)Q = (0) \subset VT$ and $UQ = (0) \subset U$. By hypothesis $QT = TQ$ and $(VQ)T = VTQ = (0)$, $VQ \subset U$. Hence $VQ = VQ^2 = (0)$ and we conclude that $V = VT \oplus U$ (Problem 6).

We claim that if $z \in VT$, then zT is a scalar multiple of z. The proof is by contradiction; suppose zT is not a scalar multiple of z and let X be a subspace containing zT such that VT is the direct sum of X and the 1-dimensional subspace spanned by z. Let R be the projection for which $(X \oplus U)R = (0)$ and $zR = z$. Then $(VT)R \subset VT$ and $UR = (0) \subset U$. Hence $RT = TR$ and $zT = zRT = (zT)R = 0$ because $zT \in X$. Therefore zT must be a scalar multiple of z.

Let z_1 and z_2 be linearly independent vectors in VT and let c_1 and c_2 be scalars such that $z_iT = c_iz_i$ for $i = 1, 2$. There is also a scalar d such that $(z_1 - z_2)T = d(z_1 - z_2) = z_1T - z_2T = c_1z_1 - c_2z_2$, and $(d - c_1)z_1 = (d - c_2)z_2$. Then $d - c_1 = d - c_2 = 0$ and $c_1 = c_2 = d$. Hence there is a scalar c such that for each $z \in VT$ we have $zT = cz$. Furthermore, $c \neq 0$ because $T \neq 0$. For each $z \in V(c^{-1}T)$ we have $z(c^{-1}T) = z$ and it follows that $c^{-1}T$ is a projection. This completes the proof.

From the argument in the preceding paragraph it is clear that if T is an operator on a vector space V and if zT is a scalar multiple of z for each $z \in V$, then T is a scalar operator.

Theorem 6. *Let T be an operator (on V) that commutes with every projection on V. Then T is a scalar operator.*

Proof. Without loss of generality we can assume that $T \neq 0$. Let U be the null space of T. Then $U = (0)$; for otherwise we can easily construct (Problem 7) a projection P for which $UP \subset U$ is false, and hence $PT \neq TP$. By Theorem 5 there is a nonzero scalar c such that cT is a projection. But the null space of cT is (0), $V(cT) = V$ and $cT = 1$.

Theorem 7. *Let P and Q be projections on V with $PQ = QP$. Then PQ is a projection with $V(PQ) = (VP) \cap (VQ)$, and $P + Q - PQ$ is a projection with $V(P + Q - PQ) = (VP) + (VQ)$.*

Proof. We have $(PQ)^2 = P(QP)Q = P(PQ)Q = PQ$, so PQ is a projection. If $z \in (VP) \cap (VQ)$, then $z(PQ) = zQ = z$ and $z \in VPQ$. If $z \in VPQ$, then $zP = (zPQ)P = (zQP)P = zQP = z$, and $zQ = (zPQ)Q = zPQ = z$, and $z \in (VP) \cap (VQ)$. Hence $VPQ = (VP) \cap (VQ)$.

Now $(P + Q - PQ)^2 = P^2 + PQ - P^2Q + QP + Q^2 - QPQ - PQP - PQ^2 + (PQ)^2 = P + Q - PQ$ and $P + Q - PQ$ is a projection. If $z \in VP$, then $z(P + Q - PQ) = zP + z(1 - P)Q = z + zP(1 - P)Q = z$ and $z \in V(P + Q - PQ)$. If $z \in VQ$, then

$z(P + Q - PQ) = zQ + z(1 - Q)P = z + zQ(1 - Q)P = z$ and
$z \in V(P + Q - PQ)$. Thus $(VP) + (VQ) \subset V(P + Q - PQ)$. On
the other hand,

$$V(P + Q - PQ) \subset VP + VQ + V(PQ)$$
$$\subset VP + VQ + VQ = VP + VQ.$$

So $V(P + Q - PQ) = (VP) + (VQ)$.

Theorem 8.   *Let P and Q be projections on V with $PQ = QP = Q$.
Then $P - Q$ is a projection and $V(P - Q) \oplus VQ = VP$.*

PROOF.   We have

$$(P - Q)^2 = P^2 - PQ - QP + Q^2 = P - Q - Q + Q = P - Q$$

and $P - Q$ is a projection.   Now $V(P - Q)P = V(P - Q) \subset VP$
and $VQP = VQ \subset VP$. Hence $V(P - Q) + VQ \subset VP$. If $z \in VP$,
then $z = zP = z(P - Q) + zQ$ and $z \in VP + V(P - Q)$. Hence
$V(P - Q) + VQ = VP$.

Select $z \in V(P - Q) \cap VQ$.   Then $z = zQ = z(P - Q) =$
$z(P - Q)Q = z(PQ - Q^2) = z(Q - Q) = 0$. Finally $V(P - Q) \oplus$
$VQ = VP$ and the proof is complete.

If P and Q are projections such that $PQ = QP = Q$ we say that
P *dominates* Q (written $Q \leq P$).   It is easy to see (Problem 8) that
$Q \leq P$ iff $VQ \subset VP$ and $V(1 - P) \subset V(1 - Q)$. If P and Q are
projections such that $PQ = QP = 0$ we say that P is *orthogonal* to Q
(written $P \perp Q$). It is easy to see (Problem 9) that $P \perp Q$ iff $VP \subset$
$V(1 - Q)$ and $VQ \subset V(1 - P)$.

If P and Q are projections it is not true that $PQ = 0$ implies
$P \perp Q$. Consider

Example 1.   Let V be a 2-dimensional vector space and let
$\{w, z\}$ be a basis of V. Define P to be the operator for which $wP = z$,
$zP = z$, and define Q to be the operator for which $wQ = w$, $zQ = 0$.
The reader can show that P and Q are projections, $PQ = 0$, but
QP is not a projection (Problem 10).

We conclude with

Theorem 9.   *Let $U_1, \ldots, U_m$ be subspaces of V such that $V =$
$\sum_i \oplus U_i$. Let P_j be the projection with range U_j and null space $\sum_{i \neq j} \oplus U_i$.
Then the projections P_j are pairwise orthogonal and $1 = \sum_j P_j$. On the
other hand, if $Q_1, \ldots, Q_m$ are pairwise orthogonal projections with $1 =$
$\sum_j Q_j$, then $V = \sum_j \oplus VQ_j$.*

PROOF.   Suppose j and k are indices, $1 \leq j < k \leq m$. Then
$VP_j = U_j, VP_k = U_k, U_j P_k = (0), U_k P_j = (0)$, and clearly $V(P_j P_k) =$
(0), $V(P_k P_j) = (0)$, and $P_j P_k = P_k P_j = 0$. If $z \in V$, then $z =$
$\sum_{i=1}^m x_i$ where $x_i \in U_i$, and for any index j, $zP_j = (\sum_{i=1}^m x_i)P_j = x_j$.
Hence $z = \sum_{j=1}^m zP_j = z(\sum_{j=1}^m P_j)$ and $\sum_j P_j = 1$.

Now $1 = \sum_j Q_j$ and if $z \in V$, then $z = z(\sum_j Q_j) = \sum_j zQ_j$, and $V = \sum_j VQ_j$. On the other hand the subspaces VQ_j are linearly independent. For if $x_j \in VQ_j$, $\sum_j x_j = 0$, we have for any index i,

$$(\textstyle\sum_j x_j) Q_i = 0 = (\sum_j x_j Q_j) Q_i = \sum_j x_j (Q_j Q_i) = x_i Q_i = x_i.$$

Problems for Lecture 3—2

1. In the proof of Theorem 1 show that there exists an operator S on V such that $U_1 S = (0)$, and $(z_i T)S = z_i$ for each $i = m + 1, \ldots, n$.

2. In the proof of Theorem 1 show in detail why dim $VS = n - m$.

3. In the proof of Theorem 1 explain in detail why TS is a projection with null space U.

4. In the proof of Theorem 1 show that ST is a projection with range VT.

5. In the proof of Theorem 4 show that the vectors $z_1 T, \ldots, z_m T$ form a basis of $V(ST)$.

6. Let T be an operator on V with null space U. Show that if $VT \cap U = (0)$, then $V = VT \oplus U$. Show that if $V = VT + U$, then $V = VT \oplus U$. Thus it was unnecessary to consider both the projections P and Q in the proof of Theorem 5. (Both projections were employed to show that Theorem 5 is valid when V is infinite dimensional. See Part 4.) Show that if W is a subspace of V, then dim $WT = \dim W - \dim (W \cap U)$.

7. If U is a nonzero subspace of V and $U \neq V$, prove that there exists a projection P that does not satisfy $UP \subset U$.

8. For projections P and Q on V show that $Q \leq P$ iff $VQ \subset VP$ and $V(1 - P) \subset V(1 - Q)$.

9. For projections P and Q on V show that $P \perp Q$ iff $VP \subset V(1 - Q)$ and $VQ \subset V(1 - P)$.

10. In Example 1 shown that P and Q are projections, $PQ = 0$, and QP is not a projection. If $P_1 P_2$ is a projection and $P_2 P_1 = 0$, must $P_1 P_2 = 0$? Explain.

11. Let $P_1, \ldots, P_m$ be projections on V with $VP_1 = \cdots = VP_m$ and let $c_1, \ldots, c_m$ be scalars such that $c_1 + \cdots + c_m = 1$. Prove that $\Sigma\, c_i P_i$ is a projection and $V(\sum_i c_i P_i) = VP_1$.

12. Let T be an operator on V and let U be a subspace of V. Prove that $UT \subset U$ if $PT = PTP$ for some projection P satisfying $VP = U$. On the other hand if $UT \subset U$ prove that $PT = PTP$ for all projections P satisfying $VP = U$.

13. Let P and Q be projections on V. Prove that $VP = VQ$ iff $PQ = P$ and $QP = Q$. Prove that $V(1 - P) = V(1 - Q)$ iff $PQ = Q$ and $QP = P$.

14. Let P and Q be projections on V and suppose that $P + Q$ is also a projection. Prove that $PQ = QP = 0$. (Hint: show that $(P + Q)^2 = P + Q$, $PQ + QP = 0$, $P(PQ + QP) = (PQ + QP)P = 0$, and $PQ = QP$.)

14'. Let P and Q be projections on V and suppose that $P - Q$ is also a projection. Prove that $PQ = QP = Q$. (Hint: show that $(P - Q)^2 = P - Q$, $2Q = PQ + QP$, $Q(PQ + QP) = (PQ + QP)Q$, $PQ = QP$.)

15. Let $P_1, \ldots, P_m$ be pairwise orthogonal projections on V. Show that there is a basis such that the matrix (a_{ij}) associated with P_k satisfies $a_{ij} = 0$ for $i \neq j$ and $a_{ii} = 1$ or 0 for each i.

16. Let T be an operator on V with $T^2 = 1$. Show that $\frac{1}{2}(T + 1)$ is a projection, and find a basis such that the matrix (a_{ij}) associated with T has $a_{ij} = 0$ for $i \neq j$ and $a_{ii} = \pm 1$ for each i.

17. Let T be an operator on V such that for every nonzero vector $z \in V$, zT is a scalar multiple of z. Prove that T is a scalar operator.

18. Let A be the matrix of an operator T (on V) relative to an ordered basis. Prove that T is nonsingular iff A is non-singular; and if they are nonsingular prove that A^{-1} is the matrix of T^{-1} relative to the same ordered basis.

19. If A is a square matrix associated with the operator T, prove that $\dim VT = \operatorname{rank} A$.

20. Fix an operator T on a vector space V and define the families M and N of operators as follows; $M = \{S: ST = 0\}$, $N = \{S: TS = 0\}$. Prove that M and N are subspaces of the vector space of all operators on V, and show that $\dim M = \dim N = (\dim V)^2 - (\dim V)(\dim VT)$.

21. Let T_1, T_2 be operators on a vector space V, and let U_1, U_2, U_3, U_4 be the null spaces of T_1, T_2, $T_1 T_2$, $T_2 T_1$, respectively.
    (a) Prove that $\dim(VT_2 T_1 + U_1) \leq \dim(VT_2 + U_1)$, and show that equality holds iff $(VT_2 T_1) \cap U_1 = (0)$.
    (b) Prove that if $\dim U_1 = \dim U_4$ and $\dim U_2 = \dim U_3$, then $VT_1 \oplus U_2 = VT_2 \oplus U_1 = V$ and $\dim U_1 = \dim U_2$. Prove that if $\dim U_1 = \dim U_3$ and $\dim U_2 = \dim U_4$, then $VT_1 \oplus U_2 = VT_2 \oplus U_1 = V$ and $\dim U_1 = \dim U_2$.
    (c) Prove that if two of the equations $\dim U_1 = \dim U_2$, $\dim U_3 = \dim U_4$, $\dim(VT_2 + U_1) = \dim(VT_1 + U_2)$ hold, then the third must also hold.

(d) Prove that $\dim (VT_1 \cap U_4) - \dim (VT_1 \cap U_2) = \dim (VT_1T_2 \cap U_1)$. (Hint: use bases.)

(e) Use $(T_1T_2)T_1 = T_1(T_2T_1)$ to derive (d).

(f) Use (d) to prove that $\dim (VT_1T_2 + U_1) \leq \dim (VT_1 + U_4) + \dim (VT_1 \cap U_2)$, and show that equality holds iff $VT_2 + U_1 = V$ and $(VT_1) \cap U_2 = (0)$.

(g) Prove that $\dim (VT_1T_2 + U_4) + \dim (VT_2T_1 + U_3) = \dim (VT_2T_1^2 + U_2) + \dim (VT_1T_2^2 + U_1) + \dim (VT_2 \cap U_1) + \dim (VT_1 \cap U_2)$.

(h) Prove that $\dim (VT_1T_2 + U_3) + \dim (VT_2T_1 + U_4) = \dim (VT_1T_2T_1 + U_2) + \dim (VT_2T_1T_2 + U_1) + \dim (VT_1 \cap U_2) + \dim (VT_2 \cap U_1)$.

$\mathcal{L}$ecture 3–3

Similar Operators, Eigenvalues, and Eigenvectors. We say that an operator S is *similar* to an operator T if there exists a non-singular operator R on V such that $RSR^{-1} = T$ (compare with the definition of similar matrices in Lecture 2-4). If S is similar to T, then T is similar to S because $RSR^{-1} = T$ implies $R^{-1}T(R^{-1})^{-1} = S$. If S is similar to T and T is similar to T_1, then S is similar to T_1, because $R_1 S R_1^{-1} = T$ and $R_2 T R_2^{-1} = T_1$ imply $(R_2 R_1) S (R_2 R_1)^{-1} = R_2 R_1 S R_1^{-1} R_2^{-1} = R_2 T R_2^{-1} = T_1$. Of course, any operator is similar to itself because $1 T 1^{-1} = T$. It follows that similarity is an equivalence relation and the set of operators on V can be divided into pairwise disjoint classes such that S is similar to T iff they are in the same class.

Let $\{z_1, \ldots, z_n\}$ be an ordered basis of V and suppose S and T are similar operators on V. In particular, there is a nonsingular operator R satisfying $RSR^{-1} = T$. Let A be the matrix of S relative to $\{z_1, \ldots, z_n\}$ and let C be the matrix of R relative to $\{z_1, \ldots, z_n\}$. Then C^{-1} is the matrix of R^{-1} and CAC^{-1} is the matrix of RSR^{-1} relative to $\{z_1, \ldots, z_m\}$. From Lecture 2-6 we see that similar operators are associated with the same matrices. The reader can easily show that S is similar to T iff S and T are associated with the same matrices (Problem 1).

If $RSR^{-1} = T$ observe that $VT = V(RSR^{-1}) = VSR^{-1}$, and hence dim $VT =$ dim VS (Problem 2). Thus the ranges of similar operators have the same dimension.

Occasionally we shall have reason to discuss similar operators on different vector spaces. If S is an operator on V and T is an operator on W we say that S is similar to T if there is a 1–1 mapping f of V onto W such that $(a_1 z_1 + a_2 z_2) f = a_1 (z_1 f) + a_2 (z_2 f)$ for any scalars a_1, a_2 and any vectors z_1, $z_2 \in V$, and $(zf) T = (zS) f$ for any $z \in V$. In the event $V = W$, f is a nonsingular operator on V and this definition of similarity agrees with the definition already given. In any case, dim $V =$ dim W if S is similar to T (Problem 3).

We say that a nonzero vector in V is an *eigenvector* of the operator T if zT is a scalar multiple of z. We say that the scalar c is the *eigenvalue* of T associated with the eigenvector z if $zT = cz$. Hence a scalar c is an eigenvalue of T if $T - c$ has nonzero null space.

74

Nonsingular operators are associated with nonsingular matrices and vice versa. Hence if A is a matrix associated with T then the scalar c is an eigenvalue of T iff c is an eigenvalue of A. In Lecture 2-4 we found a real matrix A having no real eigenvalue. Any operator T on a real vector space associated with this matrix A has no (real scalar) eigenvalue and no eigenvector. Thus an operator need not have eigenvalues or eigenvectors. However we do have

Proposition 1. *Any operator T on a complex vector space V has an eigenvalue.*

PROOF.   Let $N = \dim V$ and let z be a nonzero vector in V. Then $z, zT, zT^2, \ldots, zT^N$ are linearly dependent and there exists scalars $c_0, c_1, c_2, \ldots, c_N$, not all 0, such that $\sum_{i=0}^{N} c_i(zT^i) = z(\sum_{i=0}^{N} c_i T^i) = 0$. From Lecture 1-2 we have that there exist scalars $a_0, a_1, a_2, \ldots, a_m, a_0 \neq 0$, such that

$$\sum_{i=0}^{N} c_i x^i = a_0(x - a_1)(x - a_2)(x - a_3) \cdots (x - a_m)$$

and

$$\sum_{i=0}^{N} c_i T^i = a_0(T - a_1)(T - a_2)(T - a_3) \cdots (T - a_m).$$

Among the vectors

$$z, \ z(T - a_1), \ z(T - a_1)(T - a_2),$$
$$z(T - a_1)(T - a_2)(T - a_3), \ldots, z(T - a_1) \cdots (T - a_m)$$

the first is nonzero and the last is 0. Let w be the last nonzero vector in this list. From the following vector we see that there exists an index i with $w(T - a_i) = 0$. Hence a_i is an eigenvalue of T and w is an eigenvector associated with a_i.

Recall (Lecture 2-6) that a subspace U of V is invariant under an operator T on V if $UT \subset U$. Let T be an operator on a vector space V, and let U be a subspace invariant under T. We define the operator T' *induced* (or *implemented*) by T on the quotient space V/U as follows. For a vector $z + U$ in V/U, set $(z + U)T' = zT + U$. The mapping T' is well defined; for if $z_1 \in V$, $z_2 \in V$ such that $z_1 + U = z_2 + U$, then $z_1 - z_2 \in U$, $(z_1 - z_2)T = z_1 T - z_2 T \in U$, $z_1 T \in z_2 T + U$ and $z_1 T + U = z_2 T + U$. Furthermore T' is an operator on V/U; for if a_1, a_2 are scalars and $z_1 + U$, $z_2 + U$ are vectors in V/U, then

$$\begin{aligned}
(a_1 z_1 + a_2 z_2 + U)T' &= (a_1 z_1 + a_2 z_2)T + U \\
&= a_1(z_1 T) + a_2(z_2 T) + U \\
&= [a_1(z_1 T) + U] + [a_2(z_2 T) + U] \\
&= a_1(z_1 + U)T' + a_2(z_2 + U)T'.
\end{aligned}$$

It is important to note that T' can be defined only when U is invariant under T. This assumption was necessary to prove that T' is well defined. If S is another operator under which U is invariant, it follows that S and T induce the same operator on V/U iff $V(S - T) \subset U$ (Problem 4).

We say that an operator T on V is *nilpotent* if there exists a positive integer n such that $T^n = 0$. The *index of nilpotence* is the smallest such integer n. For example, the operator 0 is the only nilpotent operator with index 1. A square matrix A is said to be nilpotent if $A^n = 0$ for some positive integer n, and the index of nilpotence is the smallest such integer n. Clearly, nilpotent operators are associated with nilpotent matrices and vice versa. If U is a subspace invariant under a nilpotent operator T, then the operator T' induced by T on V/U is also nilpotent. In particular, if U is the null space of T, we have index $T = 1 + $ index T' (Problem 5). If T is nilpotent on V, then the contraction S of T to the subspace VT is nilpotent and index $T = 1 + $ index S (Problem 6).

Proposition 2.   *Let T be a nilpotent operator on V. Then 0 is an eigenvalue of T and T has no other eigenvalues.*

PROOF.   Let n be the index of nilpotence of T. Then $VT^n = (0)$ and $VT^{n-1} \neq (0)$. For any nonzero vector $z \in VT^{n-1}$ we have $zT = 0 = 0z$, and consequently 0 is an eigenvalue of T.

Now let a be an eigenvalue of T and let z be an eigenvector associated with a. Then $zT = az$, $zT^2 = a(zT) = a^2z$, $zT^3 = a^3z$, and so on. Finally $zT^n = a^nz = 0$ and $a = 0$ because $z \neq 0$.

Problems for Lecture 3—3

1.   Prove that the operators S and T on V are similar iff they are associated with the same matrices.

2.   Prove that the ranges of similar operators have the same dimension. Prove that the null spaces of similar operators have the same dimension.

3.   If S is an operator on V and if T is an operator on W which is similar to S, prove dim $V = $ dim W.

4.   If U is a subspace of V invariant under the operators S and T, prove that S and T induce the same operator on V/U iff $V(S - T) \subset U$.

5.   If U is a subspace invariant under a nilpotent operator T, prove that the operator T' implemented by T on V/U is nilpotent. If U is the null space of T^k prove that index $T = k + $ index T'.

6.   If T is nilpotent on V, prove that the contraction S of T to VT^k is nilpotent and index $T = k + $ index S.

7. Let U be a subspace of V invariant under the operator T and let T induce T' on V/U. Is every eigenvalue of T necessarily an eigenvalue of T'? Is every eigenvalue of T' necessarily an eigenvalue of T? Explain.

8. Suppose S and T are commuting operators on a complex vector space V. Prove that S and T have a common eigenvector. (Hint: let c be an eigenvalue of S and observe that the null space of $S - c$ is invariant under T.)

9. Let T be a nonzero nilpotent operator on V with null space U. Prove that there exists no subspace W which is complementary to U and invariant under T.

10. Let U be a subspace of V invariant under an operator T and let T' denote the contraction of T to U. Is every eigenvalue of T necessarily an eigenvalue of T'? Is every eigenvalue of T' necessarily an eigenvalue of T? Explain.

11. Let U be a subspace of V invariant under an operator T. Suppose A is a square matrix associated with the operator implemented by T on the quotient space V/U, and suppose B is a square matrix associated with the contraction of T to U. Prove that there exists a matrix C such that the operator T is associated with

$$\begin{bmatrix} A & C \\ 0 & B \end{bmatrix}$$

Lecture 3-4

Triangular and Diagonal Matrices. We say that a matrix $[a_{ij}]$ is *upper triangular* if $a_{ij} = 0$ for $j < i$; that is, all elements below the main diagonal are 0. If $\{z_1, \ldots, z_n\}$ is any ordered basis of a vector space V, then an operator T on V will be associated with an upper triangular matrix relative to this basis iff for each $i = 1, \ldots, n$, $z_i T$ is a linear combination of the vectors $z_i, z_{i+1}, \ldots, z_n$. In particular, z_n is an eigenvector for any operator associated with an upper triangular matrix. Hence on a real vector space V of dimension ≥ 2 there exist operators giving rise to an upper triangular matrix relative to *no* basis of V (see Lecture 2-4). However using complex scalars we have

Theorem 1. *Let T be an operator on a complex vector space V. Then there is an ordered basis relative to which the matrix of T is upper triangular.*

PROOF. The proof is by induction on $n = \dim V$. For $n = 1$ there is nothing to prove. Assume that the conclusion is valid on vector spaces of dimension $<n$. Let c be an eigenvalue of T. Then $V(T - c)$ is invariant under T and $\dim V(T - c) < n$ because $T - c$ has nontrivial null space (Lecture 3-2). Set $r = \dim V(T - c)$. By the inductive hypothesis there is an ordered basis $\{z_{n-r+1}, z_{n-r+2}, \ldots, z_n\}$ of $V(T - c)$ such that $z_i T$ is a linear combination of the vectors $z_i, z_{i+1}, \ldots, z_n$ for any $i = n - r + 1$, $n - r + 2, \ldots, n$. (Just consider the contraction of T to $V(T - c)$.) Extend these vectors to an ordered basis $\{z_1, \ldots, z_n\}$ of V. Then $z_i T$ is a linear combination of $z_i, z_{i+1}, \ldots, z_n$ for any $i = 1, 2, \ldots, n$. (Observe that $z_i T = cz_i + z_i(T - c)$.) This completes the induction.

A stronger result involving a family of commuting operators on V can be constructed if we employ quotient spaces. Quotient spaces, of course, could be used to prove Theorem 1 in a similar way.

Theorem 2. *Let $\mathscr{S}$ be a family of pairwise commuting operators on a complex vector space V. Then there is an ordered basis $\{z_1, \ldots, z_n\}$ of V relative to which the matrix of every operator in $\mathscr{S}$ is upper triangular.*

PROOF. By Lecture 2-6 there are finitely many operators $S_1, \ldots, S_m \in \mathscr{S}$ such that every operator in $\mathscr{S}$ is a linear combination of these. It suffices then to prove the theorem for $\{S_1, \ldots, S_m\}$. Why? (Problem 1.) Let $n = \dim V$; the proof is by induction on

78

n. For $n = 1$ there is nothing to prove; hence we assume that the theorem is valid on vector spaces of dimension $n - 1$.

Let c_1 be an eigenvalue of S_1. Then $S_1 - c_1$ has a null space $U_1 \neq (0)$, which is invariant under each S_i because each S_i commutes with $S_1 - c_1$. Let c_2 be an eigenvalue of the contraction of S_2 to U_1. Then $S_2 - c_2$ has null space U_2 with $U_1 \cap U_2 \neq (0)$ and U_2 is invariant under all the S_i. Let c_3 be an eigenvalue of the contraction of S_3 to $U_1 \cap U_2$. Then $S_3 - c_3$ has null space U_3 with $U_1 \cap U_2 \cap U_3 \neq (0)$ and U_3 is invariant under all S_i. Continuing in this way we can find a vector $z \in U_1 \cap \cdots \cap U_m$ such that z is an eigenvector for each S_i where c_i is the associated eigenvalue.

Let U be the 1-dimensional subspace spanned by z. Let S_i' be the operator induced by S_i on the quotient space V/U. Then the operators S_i' commute pairwise on V/U and dim $V/U = n - 1$. Explain (Problem 2). By the inductive hypothesis there are vectors $z_1 + U, \ldots, z_{n-1} + U$ that form an ordered basis of V/U such that $(z_i + U)S_j'$ is a linear combination of $z_i + U, \ldots, z_{n-1} + U$ for each $j = 1, \ldots, m$. Then $\{z_1, \ldots, z_{n-1}, z_n = z\}$ is an ordered basis of V for which $z_i S_j$ is a linear combination of $z_i, \ldots, z_n$ for all $j = 1, \ldots, m$. This completes the proof.

We say that the matrix $[a_{ij}]$ is *diagonal* if all the entries off the main diagonal are 0. We say that an operator T on a vector space V is *diagonable* if there is an ordered basis $\{z_1, \ldots, z_n\}$ of V that, with T, gives rise to a diagonal matrix; equivalently, each z_i is an eigenvector of T. There do exist nondiagonable operators on a complex vector space.

Example. Let V be a 2-dimensional complex vector space, let $\{z_1, z_2\}$ be a basis of V and let T be the operator for which $z_1 T = z_2$, $z_2 T = 0$. Then if $az_1 + bz_2$ is an eigenvector of T and if c is the associated eigenvalue, then $(az_1 + bz_2)T = acz_1 + bcz_2 = az_2$. Consequently $ac = 0$, $bc = a$. Clearly $c = 0$; for if $c \neq 0$ we have $a = b = 0$. Finally $a = 0$, every eigenvector of T is a scalar multiple of z_2 and T is not diagonable.

However we do have

Theorem 3. *Let T be an operator on a complex vector space V and let the (distinct) eigenvalues of T be $c_1, \ldots, c_r$. Then T is diagonable iff there exist pairwise orthogonal projections $P_1, \ldots, P_r$ such that $T = \sum_i c_i P_i$ and $1 = \sum_i P_i$.*

PROOF. First assume that the projections $P_1, \ldots, P_r$ exist as described. Form a basis of V by joining together bases of $VP_1, \ldots, VP_r$. Then each vector in this basis of V is an eigenvector of T. Explain (Problem 7).

Now assume that T is diagonable, and choose a basis of V composed of eigenvectors of T. The matrix associated with T is diagonal; let $s_{11}, \ldots, s_{nn}$ be the entries on the main diagonal.

Clearly each s_{ii} is one of the c_j. Why? (Problem 6.) For P_j it suffices to take the projection whose matrix (relative to the given basis of V) has the entry 1 in the ii-th place if $s_{ii} = c_j$ and has the entry 0 in every other place.

Before leaving Theorem 3 we observe that if T is diagonable and $T = \sum_i c_i P_i$ as stated, then $P_j = [\prod_{i \neq j} (c_j - c_i)]^{-1} \prod_{i \neq j} (T - c_i)$. Hence each P_j is a polynomial in T.

We conclude with

Theorem 4. *Let $\mathscr{S}$ be a family of pairwise commuting diagonable operators on a complex vector space V. Then there exists a basis $\{z_1, \ldots, z_n\}$ of V such that each z_i is an eigenvector of every operator in $\mathscr{S}$.*

PROOF. As in the proof of Theorem 2 we may without loss of generality assume that $\mathscr{S}$ is the finite family $\{S_1, \ldots, S_m\}$. Let $P_{i1}, P_{i2}, P_{i3}, \ldots$ be the projections given in Theorem 3 for the diagonable operator S_i. Then each P_{ij} is a polynomial in S_i and consequently the P_{ij} commute pairwise. The operators of the form $R_{i_1, i_2, \ldots, i_m} = P_{1i_1} P_{2i_2} \cdots P_{mi_m}$ are projections, and these projections are pairwise orthogonal (Problem 3). Now $P_{1i} P_{21} + P_{1i} P_{22} + P_{1i} P_{23} + \cdots = P_{1i} 1 = P_{1i}$. Repeated applications of this principle show that the sum of these projections R is 1 (Problem 4). A nonzero vector in any of the subspaces VR is necessarily an eigenvector for every S_i (why? Problem 5) and to obtain the desired basis of V we need only join together bases of these subspaces.

Problems for Lecture 3—4

1. Explain why it suffices to prove Theorem 2 only for $\{S_1, \ldots, S_m\}$.

2. In the proof of Theorem 2 explain in detail why the $S_i{}'$ commute on V/U.

3. In the proof of Theorem 4 why are the projections $R_{i_1, i_2, \ldots, i_m}$ pairwise orthogonal?

4. In the proof of Theorem 4 why is the sum of the projections $R_{i_1, i_2, \ldots, i_m}$ equal to the identity operator?

5. In the proof of Theorem 4 why is every nonzero vector in the subspace $VR_{i_1, i_2, \ldots, i_m}$ an eigenvector for each S_i?

6. In the proof of Theorem 3 why is each s_{ii} one of the c_j?

7. In the first paragraph of the proof of Theorem 3 why is each vector in the basis constructed an eigenvector of T?

8. Let A be an n by n upper triangular matrix. Show that $A^n = 0$ iff all the entries on the main diagonal of A are 0. Show that no power of A is 0 if there is a nonzero entry on the main diagonal of A. (Hint: if all the entries on the main diagonal

of A are 0, all the entries on the superdiagonal of A^2 are 0; then consider the diagonal above the superdiagonal of A^3, and so on.)

9. Let T be an operator on an n-dimensional complex vector space V. Suppose $z \in V$ such that $zT^m = 0$ for some integer $m > 0$. Prove that $zT^n = 0$. (Hint: consider an upper triangular matrix associated with the contraction of T to the null space of T^m and use Problem 8.) Use matrices to show that this is also true of real vector spaces.

9′. Problem 9 can be attacked another way. Prove that if $zT^m = 0$ for some integer $m > 0$ and if $zT^q \neq 0$, then the vectors $z, zT, zT^2, \ldots, zT^q$ are linearly independent. (Hint: suppose $\sum_{i=0}^{q} c_i zT^i = 0$, and use $\sum_{i=0}^{q} c_i zT^{i+j} = 0$ to show that all $c_i = 0$.)

10. Let T be an operator on a complex n-dimensional vector space V. Prove that there exists a diagonable operator S on V such that $(T + S)^n = 0$. (Hint: use Problem 8.)

11. Let T be an operator on an n-dimensional vector space V and let U be the null space of T^n. Prove that V is the direct sum of VT^n and U, and show that T annihilates no nonzero vector in VT^n. (Hint: use Problem 9′ to show that $(VT^n) \cap U = (0)$ and use a dimension argument.)

12. Let A be an upper triangular matrix, all of whose main diagonal entries are 0. If A is similar to a diagonal matrix, prove that $A = 0$. This problem provides us with a wealth of examples of nondiagonable operators.

13. Suppose T is diagonable on a vector space V and let U be a subspace for which $UT \subset U$. Prove that the operator induced by T on the quotient space V/U is diagonable.

Lecture 3–5

The Cayley-Hamilton Equation. Let T be an operator on a vector space V. By a *triangulation* of T we mean an upper triangular matrix that is associated with T relative to some appropriate ordered basis of V. In Lecture 3-4 we saw that T has at least one triangulation if V is complex. In general a triangulation of T is not unique (Problem 1).

Theorem 1. *Let T be an operator on a complex vector space V of dimension N, for any scalar c let V_c denote the null space of $(T - c)^N$, and let (c_{ij}) be a triangulation of T. Then $V_c = (0)$ for all but finitely many scalars c, $(c_{11} - x)(c_{22} - x) \cdots (c_{NN} - x) = \prod_c (c - x)^{\dim V_c}$, $\prod_c (c - T)^{\dim V_c} = 0$ on V, and V is the direct sum of the nonzero subspaces V_c.*

PROOF. Let $\{z_1, \ldots, z_N\}$ be an ordered basis of V that, with (c_{ij}), gives rise to the operator T. Let $(d_{ij}(s))$ be the matrix of the operator $c_{ss} - T$ relative to this basis for each $s = 1, \ldots, N$. Then $(d_{ij}(s))$ is upper triangular and $d_{ss}(s) = 0$ for each $s = 1, \ldots, N$. The entries in the first column of $(d_{ij}(1))$ are 0, the entries in the first 2 columns of $(d_{ij}(1))(d_{ij}(2))$ are 0, the entries in the first 3 columns of $(d_{ij}(1))(d_{ij}(2))(d_{ij}(3))$ are 0, and so on. Finally, all the entries in the product $(d_{ij}(1)) \cdots (d_{ij}(N))$ are 0 and $(c_{11} - T)(c_{22} - T) \cdots (c_{NN} - T) = 0$ on V.

Select a scalar d and suppose d occurs k times on the main diagonal of (c_{ij}) (possibly $k = 0$). An inspection of the matrix of the operator $d - T$ relative to our ordered basis shows that in the basis representation of the vector $z_i(d - T)^N$ the coefficient of z_i is $(d - c_{ii})^N$ and the coefficient of z_j is 0 for all $j < i$. Hence the vectors $z_i(d - T)^N$ for which $c_{ii} \neq d$ are linearly independent, $\dim V(d - T)^N \geq N - k$ and $\dim V_d \leq k$. (Explain: to show that these vectors are linearly independent note first that if $d - c_{ii} \neq 0$, then $z_i(d - T)^N$ is not a linear combination of the vectors $z_{i+1}(d - T)^N, z_{i+2}(d - T)^N, \ldots, z_N(d - T)^N$. See Problem 2.) Since there are only N entries on the main diagonal of (c_{ij}) it follows that $V_c = (0)$ for all but finitely many scalars c and $\sum_c \dim V_c \leq N$. But $\prod(c - T)^N = 0$ by the preceding paragraph, where c runs over the distinct entries on the main diagonal of (c_{ij}), and by Lecture 3-2 we have $\sum_c \dim V_c = N$. Again because there are only N entries on the main diagonal of (c_{ij}), we have $k = \dim V_d$,

82

and clearly

$$(c_{11} - x)(c_{22} - x) \cdots (c_{NN} - x) = \prod_c (c - x)^{\dim V_c}.$$

It remains only to show that V is the direct sum of all the nonzero V_c. Fix the scalar d again and set $W = V(d - T)^N$. Then $WT \subset W$, W is annihilated by $\prod_{c \neq d} (c - T)^{\dim V_c}$ and $\sum_{c \neq d} \dim (V_c \cap W) \geq \dim W$ by Lecture 3-2. But $\dim (V_c \cap W) \leq \dim V_c$, $\sum_{c \neq d} \dim V_c = N - \dim V_d = \dim W$, so $\dim (V_c \cap W) = \dim V_c$ and $V_c \subset W$ for all scalars $c \neq d$. By replacing V with W in these arguments we have $\sum_c \dim (V_c \cap W) = \dim W$; but $\dim W = N - \dim V_d = \sum_{c \neq d} \dim (V_c \cap W)$, $\dim (V_d \cap W) = 0$ and V_d contains no nonzero vector in the span of all the V_c, $c \neq d$ (Problem 3). This concludes the proof that the V_c are linearly independent. Then V is the direct sum of the nonzero V_c because $\sum_c \dim V_c = N$.

It follows from Theorem 1 that a scalar c is an eigenvalue of T iff $V_c \neq (0)$, and $V_c \neq (0)$ iff c occurs on the main diagonal of (c_{ij}). The entries on the main diagonal of any other triangulation of T are the same as the corresponding entries in (c_{ij}), the only possible difference being the order of occurrence. The polynomial $\prod_c$ $(c - x)^{\dim V_c}$ is known as the *characteristic polynomial* of T. The statement that T is annulled by its characteristic polynomial is known as the Cayley-Hamilton equation for T. Similar operators on V have the same triangulations and hence have the same characteristic polynomial.

Given an N by N matrix (a_{ij}) the characteristic polynomial p of (a_{ij}) is defined to be the characteristic polynomial of an operator on an N-dimensional complex vector space associated with (a_{ij}); equivalently $p(x) = (c_{11} - x)(c_{22} - x) \cdots (c_{NN} - x)$ for any upper triangular matrix (c_{ij}) similar to (a_{ij}). Of course, $p((a_{ij}))$ is the zero matrix. Let (d_{ij}) be a matrix such that $(a_{ij}) = (d_{ij})^{-1}(c_{ij})(d_{ij})$; by Lecture 2-5 we have

$$p(x) = \det (c_{ij} - xI_N) = \det (d_{ij})^{-1}(c_{ij} - xI_N)(d_{ij})$$
$$= \det ((d_{ij})^{-1}(c_{ij})(d_{ij}) - xI_N) = \det (a_{ij} - xI_N)$$

where I_N denotes the N by N identity matrix. (Though it is true that we used real and complex entries in Lecture 2-5, the argument goes through for entries that are polynomials in x.) The equation $p(x) = \det (a_{ij} - xI_N)$ is convenient in computing characteristic polynomials of given matrices. However the determinant did not enter the proof of Theorem 1. It follows that if all the entries a_{ij} are real, then all the coefficients in $p(x)$ are real. We define the characteristic polynomial of an operator T on a real vector space to be the characteristic polynomial of any matrix associated with T.

In Part 4 we shall have occasion to use

Theorem 2.   *Let N, V, T and V_c be as in Theorem 1 and fix a scalar d. Set $S = \prod_{c \neq d} (c - T)^N$ where c runs over the eigenvalues of $T \neq d$. Then there is a polynomial p such that $Sp(S)$ is the projection with range V_d that annihilates all the subspaces V_c, $c \neq d$.*

PROOF.   We note $VS \subset V_d$, and that if z is a nonzero vector in the null space of $d - T$ we have $zS = \prod_{c \neq d} (c - d)_{N_z \neq 0}$. If z is a nonzero vector in V_d let j be the index such that $z(d - T)^{j+1} = 0 \neq z(d - T)^j$; then $zS(d - T)^j = z(d - T)^j S \neq 0$ and $zS \neq 0$. Consequently S annihilates no nonzero vector in V_d. Let q be a nonzero polynomial such that $q(S) = 0$ on V, and let e by an index, b a nonzero scalar and r a polynomial without constant term such that $q(x) = x^e(r(x) - b)$. Then $r(S) - b$ must annihilate V_d because S^e annihilates no nonzero vector in V_d, and $zr(S) = bz$ for each $z \in V_d$. But $r(S)$ annihilates all the subspaces V_c, $c \neq d$, and clearly $b^{-1}r(S)$ is the desired projection. Now select the polynomial p such that $b^{-1}r(x) = xp(x)$.

Problems for Lecture 3—5

1.   Construct 2 similar upper triangular matrices that are not the same matrix.

2.   In the proof of Theorem 1 show in detail why those vectors $z_i(d - T)^N$ for which $c_{ii} \neq d$ are linearly independent and why $\dim V_d \leq k$.

3.   In the proof of Theorem 1 show in detail why $\dim(V_c \cap W) = \dim V_c$, $c \neq d$.

4.   In the proof of Theorem 2 show why there exists an index e, a nonzero scalar b and a polynomial $p(x)$ without constant term such that $q(x) = x^e(p(x) - b)$.

5.   Compute the characteristic polynomials of the following matrices.

$$\begin{bmatrix} 1 & 1 & 5 \\ 0 & 2 & 9 \\ 0 & 0 & 3 \end{bmatrix} \quad \begin{bmatrix} 1 & 3 \\ 2 & 5 \end{bmatrix} \quad \begin{bmatrix} 1 & 2 & 0 & 0 & 0 \\ 3 & 5 & 0 & 0 & 0 \\ 0 & 0 & 5 & 1 & 0 \\ 0 & 0 & 2 & 3 & 0 \\ 0 & 0 & 0 & 0 & 7 \end{bmatrix}$$

6.   Let z_1, z_2, z_3 be an ordered basis of a vector space V and let T be the operator for which $z_1 T = z_2$, $z_2 T = z_3$, $z_3 T = z_1$. Find the characteristic polynomial of T. Find the characteristic polynomial of the scalar operator c on an n-dimensional vector space.

7. Suppose $V = U \oplus W$ and T is an operator on V for which $UT \subset U$, $WT \subset W$. Let p (respectively q, r) be the characteristic polynomial of the contraction of T to V (respectively U, W). Prove that $p = qr$.

8. Which of the following complex matrices is diagonable?

$$A = \begin{bmatrix} 0 & 0 & 1 \\ 1 & 0 & 0 \\ 0 & 1 & 0 \end{bmatrix} \quad B = \begin{bmatrix} 0 & 0 & 1 \\ 0 & 0 & 0 \\ 1 & 0 & 0 \end{bmatrix} \quad C = \begin{bmatrix} 0 & 0 & 1 \\ 0 & 0 & 0 \\ -1 & 0 & 0 \end{bmatrix}$$

9. For n even, show that the n by n complex matrix

$$\begin{bmatrix} 0 & & & & c_1 \\ & & & c_2 & \\ & & \cdot & & \\ & \cdot & & & \\ c_n & & & & 0 \end{bmatrix}$$

is not diagonable iff for some index $i = 1, 2, \ldots, n$, we have $c_i = 0$ and $c_{n-i+1} \neq 0$. (Hint: show that this matrix is similar to the direct sum of certain 2 by 2 matrices.)

10. Work out an analogue of Problem 9 when n is odd.

11. Let T be an operator on a 2-dimensional real vector space. Prove
    (i) if T^2 has a nonnegative eigenvalue T has an eigenvalue,
    (ii) if T^2 has a negative eigenvalue, then either T has an eigenvalue or T^2 is a scalar multiple of the identity.

12. Prove that an operator on any odd dimensional real vector space has at least one eigenvalue.

13. Let T be an operator on a real or complex vector space V of dimension N. For each operator S on V, let $M(S)$ denote the dimension of the null space of S. For brevity in this problem we shall write mip in place of "monic irreducible polynomial."
    (a) Use induction on N to prove that there exists vectors $z_1, \ldots, z_m$ and mip's $p_1, \ldots, p_m$ such that $V = U_1$, $z_i \notin U_{i+1}$, $z_i p_i(T) \in U_{i+1}$ for each $i = 1, \ldots, m$, where U_i denotes the subspace of V spanned by the vectors

    $$z_i, z_i T, z_i T^2, \ldots, z_{i+1}, z_{i+1} T,$$
    $$z_{i+1} T^2, \ldots, \ldots, z_m, z_m T, z_m T^2, \ldots$$

    for each $i = 1, \ldots, m$, and $U_{m+1} = (0)$.

(Hint: to complete the induction show that there exists a mip p_m for which $M(p_m(T)) > 0$, let z_m be a nonzero vector in the null space of $p_m(T)$, and consider the operator induced by T on the quotient space V/U_m.)

(b)   Given any construction like that described in (a), show that the vectors

$$z_1, z_1 T, z_1 T^2, \ldots, z_1 T^{-1+\deg p_1}, \ldots, z_m,$$

$$z_m T, z_m T^2, \ldots, z_m T^{-1+\deg p_m}$$

form a basis of V, and $N = \sum_p k(p)(\deg p)$ where p runs over the mip's and $k(p)$ denotes the number of indices i for which $p_i = p$.

(Hint: plainly these vectors span V because $V = U_1$. If they are linearly dependent there exists a nonzero polynomial r and an index i such that $\deg r < \deg p_i$ and $z_i r(T) \in U_{i+1}$. Suppose r is a polynomial with these properties of minimal degree. Then r is a scalar; for otherwise, by the Euclidean algorithm, there exists a polynomial r_1 with r dividing $p_i - r_1$, $\deg r_1 < \deg r$, and $z_i r_1(T) \in U_{i+1}$. Hence $z_i \in U_{i+1}$, contrary to (a).)

(c)   Show that for each index $i = 1, \ldots, m$, if p_i does not divide the polynomial q, then each of the sets

$$(z_i + U_{i+1}) \cap (Vq(T)), (z_i T + U_{i+1}) \cap (Vq(T)),$$

$$\ldots, (z_i T^{-1+\deg p_i} + U_{i+1}) \cap (Vq(T))$$

is nonvoid.

(Hint: observe that $z_i p_i(T) \in U_{i+1} + Vq(T)$, $z_i q(T) \in U_{i+1} + Vq(T)$. Employ the technique used in the proof of (b) to produce a nonzero scalar c satisfying $cz_i \in U_{i+1} + Vq(T)$.)

(d)   Let q be a nonzero polynomial. For each index i for which p_i does not divide q and for each $j = 0, 1, \ldots, -1 + \deg p_i$, select a vector w_{ij} in the set $(z_i T^j + U_{i+1}) \cap (Vq(T))$. Show that the vectors w_{ij} are linearly independent and $\dim Vq(T) \geq \sum_p k(p)(\deg p)$ where p runs over the mip's that do not divide q.

(Hint: if these vectors were linearly dependent there would exist an index i and a nonzero polynomial r with $\deg r < \deg p_i$ such that $z_i r(T) \in U_{i+1}$. By the argument employed to establish (b) we can produce a nonzero scalar c such that $cz_i \in U_{i+1}$, contrary to (a).)

(e)   Prove that $M(p(T)^N) = k(p)(\deg p)$ for each mip p,
and $\sum_p M(p(T)^N) = N$ where p runs over the mip's.
(Hint: to prove $M(p(T)^N) \leq k(p)(\deg p)$ recall that
$M(p(T)^N) + \dim V[p(T)^N] = N$. Show that $\prod_p p(T)^N = 0$ and $\sum_p M(p(T)^N) \geq N = \sum_p k(p)(\deg p)$ where p runs
over the mip's p for which $k(p) > 0$.)

(f)   Let W_p denote the null space of $p(T)^N$ for each mip p.
Use (c) to prove that if z is a nonzero vector in W_p,
then there is an index i such that $z \in U_i - U_{i+1}$ and
$p_i = p$. Use an argument like the one in (d) to
prove that the nonzero W_p are linearly independent.
Then by (e) it follows that $W_p = (0)$ for all but
finitely many p, and V is the direct sum of the
nonzero W_p.

(g)   Define the *characteristic polynomial* of T to be

$$(-1)^N p_1(x) p_2(x) \cdots p_m(x).$$

Show that the characteristic polynomial of T is
independent of the choice of the z_i and p_i in (a).
Show that similar operators on V have the same
characteristic polynomial. If p is the characteristic
polynomial of T prove that $p(T) = 0$.
(Hint: if S and T are similar, then $p(S)^N$ is similar to $p(T)^N$.
The rest can be derived from (a)–(f).)

(h)   We define the characteristic polynomial of a square
matrix to be the characteristic polynomial of any
operator associated with it. Let p be the characteristic polynomial of the matrix A, let q be the
characteristic polynomial of B. Prove that pq is the
characteristic polynomial of the square matrix

$$\begin{bmatrix} A & C \\ 0 & B \end{bmatrix}$$

(Hint: consult Problem 11 of Lecture 3-3.) If (c_{ij}) is upper
triangular, prove that the characteristic polynomial of (c_{ij})
is $(c_{11} - x)(c_{22} - x) \cdots (c_{NN} - x)$. Show that our definition here of characteristic polynomial agrees with the definition in the text.

(i)   In (f) let p be a fixed mip, and set $S = \prod_q q(T)^N$
where q runs over the mip's for which $k(q) > 0$ and
$q \neq p$. Prove that there exists a polynomial r such
that $r(S)S$ is the projection with range W_p that
annihilates all the subspaces W_q, $q \neq p$.

Lecture 3--6

The Jordan Canonical Form. By a Jordan matrix we mean a matrix in which all the entries on the main diagonal are the same, all the entries on the superdiagonal are 1 and all the remaining entries are 0. In particular any 1 by 1 matrix is a Jordan matrix. In the present lecture we shall show that for any operator T on a complex vector space V there is an ordered basis of V that, with T, gives rise to a matrix equal to the direct sum (Lecture 2-4) of Jordan matrices. We begin with

Theorem 1. *Let T be a nilpotent operator on a vector space V and for each index $j = 0, 1, 2, \ldots$ let $n(j)$ denote the dimension of VT^j. Then there exist nonzero vectors $z_1, \ldots, z_r$ such that the nonzero vectors in the collection $\{z_i, z_iT, z_iT^2, \ldots\}$ form a basis of V. Furthermore, for any such basis of V and any index $j \geq 1$ the number of indices i for which $z_iT^j = 0 \neq z_iT^{j-1}$ is $n(j+1) + n(j-1) - 2n(j)$.*

PROOF. The proof of the existence of the required basis will be by induction on the index n of nilpotence of T. For $n = 1$ we have $T = 0$ and any basis of V suffices for the set $\{z_i\}$. Suppose that the required basis of V exists for nilpotent operators of index $n - 1$, and let N denote the null space of T. Then the contraction of T to the subspace VT of V is nilpotent of index $n - 1$. By the inductive hypothesis there exist vectors $v_i \in VT$ such that the nonzero vectors in $\{v_i, v_iT, \ldots\}$ form a basis of VT. For each i select $z_i \in V$ such that $z_iT = v_i$. Extend the set of nonzero vectors in

$$\{z_iT, z_iT^2, \ldots\} \cap N = \{v_i, v_iT, \ldots\} \cap N$$

to a basis of N by adjoining vectors u_j if necessary. We claim that the nonzero vectors in $\{u_j, z_i, z_iT, z_iT^2, \ldots\}$ form a basis of V. Let V' denote the subspace spanned by these vectors.

To prove independence let $w_1, \ldots, w_q$ be nonzero vectors in $\{u_j, z_i, z_iT, \ldots\}$ and $c_1, \ldots, c_q$ be nonzero scalars such that $\sum_k c_k w_k = 0$. From the equation $\sum c_k (w_kT) = 0$ it follows that all the $w_k \in N$, which is impossible.

Now let z be any vector in V. Then $zT \in VT$ and consequently zT is a linear combination of the vectors $\{z_iT, z_iT^2, \ldots\}$. It follows that there exists a vector $w \in V'$ such that $zT = wT$ (Problem 2) and $z - w \in N$. But then $z - w \in V'$ and $z = (z - w) + w \in V'$. Hence $V = V'$ and the induction is complete.

88

Now suppose that the nonzero vectors in $\{z_i, z_iT, z_iT^2, \ldots\}$ constitute a basis of V. For each $j = 0, 1, 2, \ldots$ there is a unique basis of VT^j that is a subset of this basis; indeed the basis of VT^{j+1} is a subset of the basis of VT^j. Now $n(j)$ is obviously the number of basis vectors of the form z_iT^{j+k}, $k = 0, 1, 2, \ldots$, and $n(j) - n(j + 1)$ is the number of basis vectors which are of the form z_iT^{j+k} but not of the form z_iT^{j+1+k}, and this in turn is the number of indices i for which $z_iT^j \neq 0$. It follows that for $j = 1, 2, 3, \ldots$,

$$[n(j - 1) - n(j)] - [n(j) - n(j + 1)]$$
$$= n(j + 1) + n(j - 1) - 2n(j)$$

is the number of indices i for which $z_iT^j = 0$ but $z_iT^{j-1} \neq 0$. This concludes the proof of Theorem 1.

If S is a nilpotent operator on a vector space W and if $\{z, zS, zS^2, \ldots\}$ constitutes a basis of W, then the matrix A of T relative to this ordered basis is a Jordan matrix with 0's down the main diagonal. It follows that the vectors in the basis given in Theorem 1 can be ordered such that the matrix A of T relative to this ordered basis is the direct sum of Jordan matrices with 0's down the main diagonal, and the order of each of these Jordan matrices is not less than the order of the next Jordan matrix below it. In view of the statement in Theorem 1 concerning $n(j + 1) + n(j - 1) - 2n(j)$ it follows that A is the only matrix associated with T and enjoying these properties. We call A the *Jordan Canonical Form* of T.

If T' is another nilpotent operator on a vector space V' that is similar to T, then the subspace VT^j has the same dimension as $V'T'^j$ for all j, and consequently T and T' have the same Jordan Canonical Form. Thus two nilpotent operators are similar if and only if they have the same Jordan Canonical Form.

Now let T be any operator on a complex vector space, and for each eigenvalue c of T let V_c denote the subspace of V defined in Lecture 3-5. Let $c_1, \ldots, c_r$ be the distinct eigenvalues of T. Then an ordered basis of V can be selected that, with the operator T, gives rise to a matrix equal to the direct sum of matrices $A_1, \ldots, A_r$; each A_i, in turn, is the direct sum of Jordan matrices with c_i on their main diagonals and such that the order of each Jordan matrix is not less than the order of the next one below it. What basis? (Problem 5.) This direct sum is known as the *Jordan Canonical Form* of T. (For a nilpotent operator this definition coincides with the previous definition of Jordan Canonical Form.) It is uniquely defined except for the order in which the eigenvalues of T are taken.

If T' is another operator on a complex vector space V', similar to T, then the contraction of $T - c_i$ to V_{c_i} is similar to the contraction of $T' - c_i$ to V_{c_i}' and T and T' have the same Jordan Canonical

Form. Thus two operators on complex vector spaces are similar if and only if they have the same Jordan Canonical Form. In particular, an operator is diagonable if and only if its Jordan Canonical Form is a diagonal matrix.

A generalization of Theorem 1 to infinite dimensional vector spaces will be discussed in Lecture 4-5.

Problems for Lecture 3—6

1. In the proof of Theorem 1 why must all the w_k be in N?
2. In the proof of Theorem 1 explain why for any $z \in V$, there exists a $w \in V'$ such that $zT = wT$.
3. In the proof of Theorem 1 explain in detail why $n(j) - n(j+1)$ is the number of indices i for which $z_i T^j \neq 0$.
4. If T and T' are similar why do VT^j and $V'T'^j$ have the same dimension?
5. For an arbitrary operator on a complex vector space V show in detail how an ordered basis of V can be selected so that it gives rise to the Jordan Form of T.
6. Show that a nonzero nilpotent 2 by 2 complex matrix is similar to $\begin{bmatrix} 0 & 1 \\ 0 & 0 \end{bmatrix}$.
7. Show that a nonzero nilpotent 3 by 3 complex matrix is similar to exactly one of the matrices

$$\begin{bmatrix} 0 & 1 & 0 \\ 0 & 0 & 0 \\ 0 & 0 & 0 \end{bmatrix} \qquad \begin{bmatrix} 0 & 1 & 0 \\ 0 & 0 & 1 \\ 0 & 0 & 0 \end{bmatrix}$$

8. Show that a nonzero nilpotent 4 by 4 complex matrix is similar to exactly one of the matrices

$$\begin{bmatrix} 0 & 1 & 0 & 0 \\ 0 & 0 & 0 & 0 \\ 0 & 0 & 0 & 0 \\ 0 & 0 & 0 & 0 \end{bmatrix} \begin{bmatrix} 0 & 1 & 0 & 0 \\ 0 & 0 & 1 & 0 \\ 0 & 0 & 0 & 0 \\ 0 & 0 & 0 & 0 \end{bmatrix} \begin{bmatrix} 0 & 1 & 0 & 0 \\ 0 & 0 & 1 & 0 \\ 0 & 0 & 0 & 1 \\ 0 & 0 & 0 & 0 \end{bmatrix} \begin{bmatrix} 0 & 1 & 0 & 0 \\ 0 & 0 & 0 & 0 \\ 0 & 0 & 0 & 1 \\ 0 & 0 & 0 & 0 \end{bmatrix}$$

9. Construct analogues of Problems 6, 7, and 8 for nilpotent 5 by 5 and 6 by 6 matrices.

10. Show that these complex matrices are similar.

$$\begin{bmatrix} 0 & 1 & 0 & 0 \\ 0 & 0 & 1 & 0 \\ 0 & 0 & 0 & 1 \\ 0 & 0 & 0 & 0 \end{bmatrix} \cdot \quad \begin{bmatrix} 0 & 2 & 5 & -6 \\ 0 & 0 & i & 44 \\ 0 & 0 & 0 & 3i \\ 0 & 0 & 0 & 0 \end{bmatrix}$$

11. Suppose the characteristic polynomial of the operator T on a 14-dimensional complex vector space V is

$$(5 - \lambda)^3(3 - \lambda)^3(2 - \lambda)^3(-1 - \lambda)^2(-5 - \lambda)^2(8 - \lambda).$$

   Let $N(S)$ denote the null space of the operator S. Let the dim $N(5 - T) = 1$, dim $N(3 - T) = 2$, dim $N(2 - T) = 3$, dim $N(-1 - T) = 2$, dim $N(-5 - T) = 1$. Write the Jordan Form of T.

12. Use the technique you employed in Problem 11 to find the Jordan Forms of the matrices

$$\begin{bmatrix} 1 & 0 & 1 \\ 0 & 0 & 0 \\ 0 & 0 & -1 \end{bmatrix} \quad \begin{bmatrix} 0 & 1 & 0 & 0 & 0 \\ 1 & 0 & 1 & 0 & 0 \\ 0 & 1 & 0 & 0 & 0 \\ 0 & 0 & 0 & 0 & 0 \\ 0 & 0 & 0 & 5 & 0 \end{bmatrix}$$

13. Show that an operator T on a complex vector space is not diagonable iff there exists an eigenvalue c and a vector z such that $z(T - c)^2 = 0 \neq z(T - c)$. (Hint: use the Jordan Form.)

14. Suppose T is a diagonable operator on V and U is a subspace of V such that $UT \subset U$. Prove that T is diagonable on U.

15. Suppose T is an operator on V, and U_1 and U_2 are subspaces satisfying $U_1T \subset U_1$, $U_2T \subset U_2$. Then the contraction of T to $U_1 + U_2$ is diagonable iff the contractions of T to U_1 and U_2 are each diagonable.

Part 4   INFINITE-
DIMENSIONAL
VECTOR SPACES

$\mathcal{L}ecture$ 4–1

Introduction. In the present part we drop the requirement that the vector space be spanned by a finite set of elements. Vector spaces not satisfying this property, of course, cannot have finite bases; consequently they are called infinite-dimensional. One example of an infinite-dimensional vector space is the family of real (or complex) polynomials in x under the usual operations of addition and scalar multiplication of polynomials.

Many of the properties enjoyed by operators on finite-dimensional vector spaces are not in general true for operators on infinite-dimensional vector spaces. For example, in Lecture 4-4 we shall see that such an operator need not be annulled by a nontrivial polynomial. Operators that are annulled by a nontrivial polynomial are called *algebraic*. Algebraic operators and some classical results on operators commuting with algebraic operators are studied in Lectures 4-4 and 4-6. In Lecture 4-5 we present results on nilpotent operators, which can be regarded as generalizations of Theorem 1 of Lecture 3-6 on the Jordan Form. We define an *algebra* of operators to be a nonvoid family M of operators on a vector space such that for any S, $T \in M$ and for any scalars a, b we have $aS + bT \in M$ and $ST \in M$. Lectures 4-2 and 4-7 give some of the classic results concerning operator algebras including the theorems of Schur and Burnside.

In this Part we shall employ the Maximum Principle and the Choice Axiom we discussed in Lecture 1-1. We shall use the Choice Axiom so frequently that applications of it will not usually be identified.

As in the case of finite-dimensional vector spaces we say that a collection of vectors $\{v_\alpha\}$ in a vector space V is a basis of V if it is linearly independent and any vector $v \in V$ is a linear combination of the vectors in $\{v_\alpha\}$ (of course, in this linear combination the coefficient of v_α is 0 for all but finitely many α). We use the Maximum Principle to prove

Theorem 1. *A real or complex vector space V has a basis.*

PROOF. Let $\{E_\alpha\}$ be the family of all linearly independent subsets of V. The void set is in $\{E_\alpha\}$ so evidently $\{E_\alpha\}$ is nonvoid. If $\{S_\beta\}$ is a nest of sets in $\{E_\alpha\}$ we claim that $U_\beta S_\beta$ is linearly independent.

95

To see this suppose that $z_i \in U_\beta S_\beta$ and $\sum_i c_i z_i = 0$ for some scalars c_i. Then $z_i \in S_{\beta_i}$, say, and among the finitely many subsets S_{β_i} there is one S_β of which all the S_{β_i} are subsets, and all the $z_i \in S_\beta$. Because S_β is linearly independent we have $c_i = 0$ for all i.

From the Maximum Principle it follows that there exists a maximal linearly independent set E; i.e., if E_0 is a linearly independent set such that $E \subset E_0$, then $E = E_0$. We claim that E is a basis of V. To see this let $v \in V - E$. Then the set $\{v\} \cup E$ is linearly dependent and $cv + \sum_i c_i z_i = 0$ where $z_i \in E$ and not all the scalars c, c_i are 0. Furthermore $c \neq 0$; for otherwise $\sum_i c_i z_i = 0$, not all the $c_i = 0$, and E would be linearly dependent. So $v = \sum_i - c^{-1} c_i z_i$, and this linear combination of vectors in E is unique because E is linearly independent. Explain (Problem 3). (By a similar argument the reader can easily show that any linearly independent set of vectors in V can be extended to a basis of V.)

A comparison of this proof with the proof of the same theorem for finite-dimensional vector spaces given in Lecture 2-2 shows that the only new concept needed here is the Maximum Principle, which we employ to produce a maximal linearly independent set of vectors. For an example, consider again the vector space of polynomials in x with real or complex scalars. Then the vectors $1, x, x^2, x^3, \ldots$ obviously form a basis, and this basis is countably infinite.

Now let V be a real or complex vector space with a countably infinite basis $\{z_1, z_2, z_3, \ldots\}$, let S be the operator on V for which $z_1 S = 0$, $z_i S = z_{i-1}$ for $i > 1$, and let T be the operator for which $z_i T = z_{i+1}$ for all i. Then $z_1 ST = 0$ and $z_i TS = z_i$ for all i. It follows that $TS = 1$ and $ST \neq 1$. Note also that the null space of T is (0) but $VT \neq V$; the null space of S is not (0) but $VS = V$. In general the results stated in Part 3 do not hold in the infinite-dimensional case. On the other hand a review of Lectures 3-1, 3-2, 3-3, and 3-6 will show that much work therein does carry over to infinite-dimensional vector spaces (Problem 5).

An operator S for which there exists an operator T satisfying $ST = TS = 1$ is said to be *invertible*, and T is called the *inverse* of S (denoted S^{-1}). Similarly S is the inverse of T. The preceding paragraph shows that on an infinite-dimensional vector space $TS = 1$ does not imply that S or T is invertible.

Problems for Lecture 4—1

1. Let M be an operator algebra on a vector space V and let $z \in V$. Show that the set of vectors zM forms a subspace of V, and show that zM is the smallest subspace of V invariant under M and containing z (i.e., if U is a subspace invariant under M and containing z then $zM \subset U$.)

2. Let T be an operator on a vector space V and let $z \in V$. Show that the vectors $z, zT, zT^2, zT^3, \ldots$ span the smallest sub-space of V invariant under T and containing z.

3. In the proof of Theorem 1 explain why the linear combination $\sum_i c^{-1} c_i z_i$ is unique.

4. Prove that a linearly independent set of vectors in a vector space V can be extended to a basis of V.

5. Determine which of the results stated in Part 3 carry over to infinite-dimensional vector spaces.

6. Prove that the vector space of all polynomials in x over the real or complex field is not finite-dimensional.

7. Prove that any operator algebra contains the operator 0, and is itself a vector space.

$\mathcal{L}ecture$ 4–2

Commutants. Let M be any nonvoid family of operators on a real or complex vector space V. By the *commutant* of M (denoted M') we mean the set of all operators on V that commute with every operator in M. The reader can easily show that M' is closed under products and linear combinations; i.e., M' is an operator algebra. Likewise M'', the commutant of M', is an operator algebra, and in general $M^{(n)}$, the commutant of $M^{(n-1)}$, is an operator algebra. We call M'' the *bicommutant* of M. Since every operator in M commutes with every operator in M' we have that $M \subset M''$. Indeed $M \subset M'' \subset M^{(4)} \subset M^{(6)} \subset \cdots$ and $M' \subset M''' \subset M^{(5)} \subset \cdots$. Since an operator commuting with every operator in $M^{(n+2)}$ must also commute with every operator in $M^{(n)}$, we have that $M'' = M^{(4)} = M^{(6)} = \cdots$ and $M' = M''' = M^{(5)} = \cdots$.

The question arises: if M is an operator algebra, must $M = M''$? That this equality does not hold in general follows from the

Example. Let V be a 2-dimensional vector space and let U be a 1-dimensional subspace of V. Let M consist of the family of all operators on V under which U is invariant. Clearly M is an operator algebra. Explain (Problem 6). A basis for V can be selected such that M consists of all operators associated with the matrices $[a_{ij}]$ where $a_{21} = 0$. How?

Now suppose an operator in M' is associated with the matrix $[c_{ij}]$. Then

$$\begin{bmatrix} c_{11} & 0 \\ c_{21} & 0 \end{bmatrix} = \begin{bmatrix} c_{11} & c_{12} \\ c_{21} & c_{22} \end{bmatrix}\begin{bmatrix} 1 & 0 \\ 0 & 0 \end{bmatrix} = \begin{bmatrix} 1 & 0 \\ 0 & 0 \end{bmatrix}\begin{bmatrix} c_{11} & c_{12} \\ c_{21} & c_{22} \end{bmatrix} = \begin{bmatrix} c_{11} & c_{12} \\ 0 & 0 \end{bmatrix}$$

$$\begin{bmatrix} 0 & c_{11} \\ 0 & c_{21} \end{bmatrix} = \begin{bmatrix} c_{11} & c_{12} \\ c_{21} & c_{22} \end{bmatrix}\begin{bmatrix} 0 & 1 \\ 0 & 0 \end{bmatrix} = \begin{bmatrix} 0 & 1 \\ 0 & 0 \end{bmatrix}\begin{bmatrix} c_{11} & c_{12} \\ c_{21} & c_{22} \end{bmatrix} = \begin{bmatrix} c_{21} & c_{22} \\ 0 & 0 \end{bmatrix}$$

and it follows that $c_{11} = c_{22}$ and $c_{21} = c_{12} = 0$. Thus M' consists of only the scalar operators and M'' is composed of all operators on V. Hence $M \neq M''$.

We make the following

Definition. *Let M be a family of operators on V. We say that M is completely reducible if the null space of M is (0) and if with every subspace*

98

U of V invariant under M, there is a subspace W of V invariant under M and complementary to U.

It follows that if M is completely reducible and if U is a subspace invariant under M, then there exists a projection P in M' for which $VP = U$. To see this let P be the operator with null space W and mapping every vector in U into itself.

The algebra of all operators on V and the algebra of scalar operators on V are completely reducible. On the other hand the algebra in the preceding example is not completely reducible because there is no subspace complementary to U which is invariant under M. Explain (Problem 6). We present the

Theorem 1 (**Dieudonné**). *Let M be a completely reducible operator algebra. Then any operator $S \in M''$ can be approximated by operators in M in the following sense; given any finite set of vectors $\{z_1, \ldots, z_n\}$ there is an operator $T \in M$ for which $z_i T = z_i S$, for each i. In particular, if V is finite dimensional, we have $M = M''$.*

The proof of Theorem 1 will be developed in a series of Lemmas. Until further notice assume that the hypotheses are satisfied.

Lemma 1. *For any vector $z \in V$, there is a $T \in M$ such that $zT = z$.*

PROOF. The subspace zM is invariant under M and consequently there is a subspace U complementary to zM and invariant under M. Put $z = x + y$ where $x \in zM$ and $y \in U$.

The proof is by contradiction; suppose z is not in zM. Then $y \neq 0$; because (0) is the null space of M there is a $T \in M$ for which $yT \neq 0$. It follows that $zT = xT + yT$, $xT \in zM$, $yT \notin zM$, and $zT \notin zM$, which is impossible. This completes the proof.

Lemma 2. *Any subspace of V invariant under M is invariant under M''.*

PROOF. Let U be a subspace invariant under M; then there is a subspace W complementary to U and also invariant under M. Let P be the projection with range U and null space W; then $P \in M'$. Hence VP and W are invariant under every operator in M''.

Lemma 3. *With any $z \in V$ and any $S \in M''$, there is a $T \in M$ for which $zT = zS$.*

PROOF. By Lemma 1 z is in zM. By Lemma 2 zM is invariant under M'', and consequently $zS \in zM$. The conclusion is evident.

We intend to show that for any finite set $\{z_1, \ldots, z_n\}$ of vectors and for any $S \in M''$, there is a $T \in M$ for which $z_i T = z_i S$, $i = 1, \ldots, n$. The proof is by induction on n. Lemma 3 proves the conclusion for $n = 1$; *assume the conclusion is valid for $n = m - 1$ in all that follows.*

Lemma 4. *If $z_1, \ldots, z_m$ are vectors such that $z_1 T = z_2 T = \cdots = z_{m-1} T = 0$ implies $z_m T = 0$ for all $T \in M$, then $z_1 S = z_2 S = \cdots = z_{m-1} S = 0$ implies $z_m S = 0$ for all $S \in M''$.*

PROOF. The proof is by contradiction. Suppose $S \in M''$ and $z_1 S = z_2 S = \cdots = z_{m-1} S = 0$, $z_m S \neq 0$, but $z_1 T = z_2 T = \cdots = z_{m-1} T = 0$ implies $z_m T = 0$ for all $T \in M$. Let N be the algebra of all operators annihilating the vectors $z_2, \ldots, z_{m-1}$. (Of course, if $m = 2$, let N be the algebra of all operators on V.) Let U be the subspace (of V) composed of all vectors $z_1 T$ where $T \in M \cap N$. It follows that U is invariant under M; if $T \in M$ and $T' \in M \cap N$, then $T'T \in M \cap N$ and $(z_1 T')T \in U$. There is a subspace W invariant under M and complementary to U. There is a $P \in M \cap N$ for which $z_1 - z_1 P \in W$. Why? (Problem 1.) Then for any $T \in M \cap N$ the vector $(z_1 - z_1 P)T = z_1(T - PT) \in U \cap W$ and $(z_1 - z_1 P)T = 0$. By the inductive hypothesis there exists a $T \in M \cap N$ for which $(z_1 - z_1 P)S = (z_1 - z_1 P)T = 0$; hence $z_1 PS = 0$.

For any operator $T \in M \cap N$, $z_1(T - PT) = 0$ and (because $T - PT \in M \cap N$) $z_m(T - PT) = 0$ by assumption. By the inductive hypothesis there is a $T \in M \cap N$ for which $(z_m - z_m P)S = (z_m - z_m P)T = 0$; hence $z_m PS \neq 0$.

We construct the operator C on V as follows. If $y \in W$ put $yC = 0$; if $y = z_1 T$ for some $T \in M \cap N$ put $yC = z_m T$. Now C is well-defined, for if $z_1 T_1 = z_1 T_2$ for operators $T_1, T_2 \in M \cap N$, then $z_1(T_1 - T_2) = 0$, $z_m(T_1 - T_2) = 0$ and $z_m T_1 = z_m T_2$. Plainly C is an operator; we claim that $C \in M'$. To prove this let $T \in M$. Then if $y \in W$ we have $yCT = (0)T = 0 = (yT)C$ because $yT \in W$; on the other hand if $y = z_1 T'$ for some $T' \in M \cap N$ we have

$$yCT = (z_1 T'C)T = z_m T'T = (z_1 T'T)C = yTC$$

because $T'T \in M \cap N$. Consequently $CT = TC$ on V and $C \in M'$. But $S \in M''$ and consequently $SC = CS$. In particular

$$0 = (z_1 PS)C = (z_1 P)CS = z_m PS \neq 0$$

which is impossible. This completes the proof of Lemma 4.

Lemma 5. *If $z_1, \ldots, z_m$ are vectors and if S is an operator in M'' for which $z_1 S = \cdots = z_{m-1} S = 0$, then there is an operator $T \in M$ for which $z_1 T = \cdots = z_{m-1} T = 0$ and $z_m T = z_m S$.*

PROOF. Let $z_1, \ldots, z_m$ and S be as described and let U be the subspace of V composed of all vectors $z_m T$ where T is an operator in M for which $z_1 T = \cdots = z_{m-1} T = 0$. Then U is invariant under M, for if $T' \in M$ and if T is as before then $z_1 TT' = \cdots = z_{m-1} TT' = 0$ and $z_m TT' \in U$.

The proof is by contradiction; suppose there is no such operator T described in the conclusion. Then $z_m \notin U$ because U is invariant under S. Explain (Problem 10). Let W be a subspace complementary to U, and invariant under M and, therefore, under M''. Then $z_m = u + w$ where $u \in U$, $w \in W$, and $w \neq 0$. Now $wS \neq 0$

because $z_m S \notin U$; consequently there is an $R \in M$ for which $z_1 R = \cdots = z_{m-1} R = 0$ and $wR \neq 0$ by Lemma 4. Then $z_m R = uR + wR$, $uR \in U$, $wR \notin U$, and $z_m R \notin U$ contrary to the definition of U. The proof of Lemma 5 is complete.

PROOF OF THEOREM 1.   Let $S \in M''$ and let $z_1, \ldots, z_m$ be vectors. By the inductive hypothesis there is a $T \in M$ for which $z_i T = z_i S$, $i = 1, \ldots, m - 1$. Then $z_i (S - T) = 0$, $i = 1, \ldots, m - 1$ and $S - T \in M''$. By Lemma 5 there is an $R \in M$ for which $z_i R = 0$, $i = 1, \ldots, m - 1$, and $z_m (S - T) = z_m R$. It follows that $z_i (R + T) = z_i S$, $i = 1, \ldots, m$, and $R + T \in M$. This concludes the proof of Theorem 1. Note also that if V is finite-dimensional we have $M = M''$ by making $\{z_1, \ldots, z_n\}$ a basis of V.

We now turn to a type of family of operators more restrictive than the completely reducible families.

Definition.   *We say that a family of operators M on a vector space V is irreducible if $M \neq (0)$ and if the only subspaces of V invariant under M are V and (0).*

Clearly the algebra M is irreducible iff $V = zM$ for each nonzero $z \in V$. Explain (Problem 17). If M is irreducible, plainly M is also completely reducible. However there do exist completely reducible families that are not irreducible. Find an example (Problem 2).

Theorem 2 (Schur).   *Let M be an irreducible family of operators on a vector space V and let S be an operator on V for which $SM = MS$. Then either $S = 0$ or S is invertible.*

PROOF.   Suppose $SM = MS$ and $S \neq 0$. If $z \in V$ and $zS = 0$ we have $(zM)S = (zS)M = (0)$. Also $(VS)M = (VM)S \subset VS$ and it is plain that the range and null space of S are both subspaces invariant under M. Then V is the range of S and (0) is the null space of S; i.e., S is a 1–1 mapping of V onto V. This completes the proof.

Theorem 3 (Burnside).   *Let M be an irreducible operator algebra on a complex finite-dimensional vector space V. Then M is composed of all the operators on V.*

PROOF.   Let $S \in M'$. There exists an eigenvalue c of S, and $S - c$ is not invertible. But $(S - c)M = M(S - c)$, and by Theorem 2 $S - c = 0$ and $S = c$. Thus M' consists only of the scalar operators and M'' is composed of all the operators on V. Furthermore the null space of M is invariant under M and must consequently be (0). The conclusion follows from Theorem 1 because M is irreducible and, therefore, completely reducible.

In the same way we can also prove the

Corollary.   *Let M be an irreducible family of operators on a finite-dimensional complex vector space V. Then M' consists only of the scalar operators.*

Problems for Lecture 4—2

1. In the proof of Lemma 4 explain why there exists an operator $P \in M \cap N$ for which $z_1 - z_1 P \in W$. (Hint: let $z_1 = u + w$ where $w \in W$ and $u \in U$. Say $u = z_1 T$, $T \in M \cap N$.)

2. Show that the algebra of all operators on V is irreducible, and that the algebra of scalar operators on V is completely reducible but not in general irreducible.

3. Let M be the smallest algebra of operators containing the family of operators N on V. Show that M is completely reducible iff N is. Show that M is irreducible iff N is.

3'. If M is completely reducible and if N is the smallest operator algebra containing M and 1, show that N is also completely reducible. If M is irreducible show that N is also.

4. If M is a completely reducible set of operators on V show that M'' is also completely reducible. If M is irreducible show that M'' is also.

5. If M is a completely reducible operator algebra on V show that with any vectors $z_1, \ldots, z_n$ in V there is a $T \in M$ for which $z_i = z_i T$ for all i.

6. Explain why M in the example is an operator algebra. Explain why there is no subspace W complementary to U and invariant under M.

7. If M is an irreducible family of operators on V, show that $V = VM$ and the null space of M is (0).

8. In the proof of Lemma 4 explain why U is closed under linear combinations.

9. In the proof of Lemma 4 explain why C is an operator.

10. In the proof of Lemma 5 explain why $z_m \notin U$.

11. Let M be the operator algebra on an infinite-dimensional vector space V composed of all the operators T for which VT is finite-dimensional. Show that M is irreducible, but $M \neq M''$.

12. An operator algebra M on a vector space V is said to be *n-fold transitive* if for each $k \leq n$, for vectors $x_1, \ldots, x_k$ and for linearly independent vectors $z_1, \ldots, z_k$, there exists a $T \in M$ for which $x_j = z_j T$, $j = 1, \ldots, k$. Show that if M is 2-fold transitive, then M is n-fold transitive for any integer $n > 0$. (Hint: show first that M is irreducible and that M' is composed of only the scalar operators.)

13. Let V be a 2-dimensional vector space with basis $\{z_1, z_2\}$ and let T be that operator for which $z_1 = z_2 T$, $z_1 T = 0$. Show that the set of operators M of the form $aT + b$, a, b scalar,

is an operator algebra with $M = M'$. Show also that M is not completely reducible. (Thus a commutant need not be completely reducible.)

14. If M and N are families of operators on V such that $M \subset N$, prove that $N' \subset M'$. Does $N' = M'$ imply $N = M$?

15. Let M be a commutative family of operators on V (i.e., any two operators in M commute). Show that $M \subset M'$. By the Maximum Principle show that M is a subset of a commutative operator algebra N which is not a subalgebra of a larger commutative algebra N_1 such that $M \subset N_1$. Prove $N = N'$.

16. Let M be an operator algebra on V for which $M = M'$. Prove that M is a commutative operator algebra and that M is not a subalgebra of a larger commutative operator algebra.

17. Prove that the algebra M is irreducible iff $V = zM$ for each nonzero $z \in V$. (Hint: zM is invariant under M.)

$\mathcal{L}$ecture 4–3

Nilpotent Operators and Simultaneous Bases. Let T be a nilpotent operator on a vector space V. It follows that there exists a family of vectors $\{z_\alpha\}$ such that the nonzero vectors in the collection $\{z_\alpha, z_\alpha T, z_\alpha T^2, \ldots\}$ constitute a basis of V. The required argument is essentially the same as in the proof of Theorem 1 of Lecture 3-6 in which the Maximum Principle is employed to extend a linearly independent set of vectors to a basis of a vector space. Now suppose U is a subspace of V and invariant under T. The question arises whether or not there exists a family of vectors $\{z_\alpha\}$ in V such that the nonzero vectors in the collection $\{z_\alpha, z_\alpha T, z_\alpha T^2, \ldots\}$ constitute a basis of V and the nonzero vectors in $\{z_\alpha, z_\alpha T, z_\alpha T^2, \ldots\} \cap U$ constitute a basis of U. For convenience in this lecture we shall call such a basis a *simultaneous basis* of U and V under T. That U and V do not in general have a simultaneous basis under T is shown by

Example 1. Let V be a 4-dimensional vector space with basis $\{z_1, z_2, z_3, z_4\}$ and let T be the operator on V for which $z_1 T = z_2$, $z_2 T = z_3$, $z_3 T = 0$, $z_4 T = z_3$. Let U be the subspace spanned by the vectors z_3 and z_4. Then T is nilpotent on V, and U is invariant under T. We claim that there exists no simultaneous basis of U and V under T. For otherwise such a basis would contain vectors $\sum_1^4 a_i z_i$ and $\sum_3^4 b_i z_i$ where $a_1 \neq 0$, $b_4 \neq 0$, and would also contain $\left(\sum_1^4 a_i z_i\right) T^2 = a_1 z_3$ and $\left(\sum_3^4 b_i z_i\right) T = b_4 z_3$. But $\left(\sum_1^4 a_i z_i\right) T \neq \sum_3^4 b_i z_i$, which is impossible.

In the present lecture we shall give a necessary and sufficient condition that U and V have a simultaneous basis under T. We begin with

Lemma 1. *Suppose U and V have a simultaneous basis under T. Then for any integers $n, m > 0$ we have $(U \cap VT^n) T^m = UT^m \cap VT^{n+m}$.*

PROOF. The inclusion $(U \cap VT^n) T^m \subset UT^m \cap VT^{n+m}$ is clear. To prove the reverse inclusion suppose $u \in UT^m \cap VT^{n+m}$. Then $u \in U$ and there are vectors $u_1, \ldots, u_r$ in the given basis of U for which $u = \sum_1^r a_i u_i$. But also $u \in VT^{n+m}$. It is clear that there exist vectors $v_1, \ldots, v_r$ in the basis of V such that $u_i = v_i T^{n+m}$ for all $i = 1, \ldots, r$. Furthermore there exist u_i' in the basis of U for which $u_i = u_i' T^m$ for all $i = 1, \ldots, r$, because $u \in UT^m$. It follows that $u_i' = v_i T^n$ for all $i = 1, \ldots, r$, and $u = \sum_1^r a_i u_i' T^m \in (U \cap VT^n) T^m$. This concludes the proof.

Lemma 2. *Suppose $U \subset N$ where N is the null space of T. Then U and V have a simultaneous basis under T.*

PROOF. We use induction on the index q of nilpotence of T. If $q = 1$, then $T = 0$ and we need only extend a basis of U to a basis of V. Assume Lemma 2 is valid for nilpotent operators of index $q - 1$. Then $VT \cap U$ and VT have a simultaneous basis under T, say $\{v_\alpha, v_\alpha T, v_\alpha T^2, \ldots\}$. Extend the set of nonzero vectors in $\{v_\alpha, v_\alpha T, \ldots\} \cap U$ to a basis of U by adjoining vectors $\{u_\beta\}$ if necessary, and then extend the set of nonzero vectors in

$$[\{u_\beta\} \cup \{v_\alpha, v_\alpha T, v_\alpha T^2, \ldots\}] \cap N$$

to a basis of N by adjoining vectors $\{x_\gamma\}$ if necessary. For each α choose $z_\alpha \in V$ such that $z_\alpha T = v_\alpha$. Then the nonzero vectors in $\{x_\gamma\} \cup \{u_\beta\} \cup \{z_\alpha, z_\alpha T, z_\alpha T^2, \ldots\}$ form a basis of V by essentially the argument in the proof of Theorem 1 of Lecture 3-6. This completes the induction and Lemma 2 is proved.

We are now able to give a condition equivalent to the existence of a simultaneous basis for U and V under T.

Theorem 1. *Let T be a nilpotent operator on a vector space V and let U be a subspace of V invariant under T. Then a necessary and sufficient condition that U and V have a simultaneous basis under T is that for all integers $n, m > 0$, $(U \cap VT^n)T^m = UT^m \cap VT^{n+m}$.*

PROOF. Lemma 1 shows that the condition is necessary. To prove sufficiency suppose that the condition holds. The proof that U and V have a simultaneous basis under T will be by induction on the index q of nilpotence of T on U. If $q = 1$, the conclusion follows from Lemma 2. Suppose Theorem 1 is valid for nilpotent operators of index $q - 1$ on U. For integers $n, m > 0$,

$$[UT \cap VT^n]T^m = [U \cap VT^{n-1}]T^{m+1} = (UT)T^m \cap VT^{n+m}$$

and it follows from the inductive hypothesis that UT and V have a simultaneous basis under T, say $\{v_\alpha, v_\alpha T, v_\alpha T^2, \ldots\}$. Let N denote the null space of T.

Let W be the subspace spanned by all the vectors $v_\alpha, v_\alpha T, v_\alpha T^2$, $\ldots$ for those indices α for which none of the nonzero vectors among $v_\alpha, v_\alpha T, v_\alpha T^2, \ldots$ lie in UT. It follows that $U \cap N = (U \cap W) \oplus (UT \cap N)$. Explain (Problem 2). We use Lemma 2 to redefine those vectors v_α in W so that the span of the vectors

$$\{v_\alpha, v_\alpha T, v_\alpha T^2, \ldots\} \cap (U \cap N)$$

contains $U \cap W$, and hence contains $U \cap N$.

For each index α define the vector $z_\alpha \in V$ as follows. If there exists a positive integer n such that $v_\alpha T^n \neq 0$, $v_\alpha T^n \in UT$, $v_\alpha T^{n-1} \notin UT$ select $z_\alpha \in V$ such that $z_\alpha T^n = v_\alpha T^n$ and $z_\alpha T^{n-1} \in U$; the existence of z_α follows from $UT \cap VT^n = [U \cap VT^{n-1}]T$. If $v_\alpha \in W$, set $z_\alpha - v_\alpha$. Note that the nonzero vectors in $\{z_\alpha, z_\alpha T, z_\alpha T^2, \ldots\} \cap (UT)$ form a basis of UT. We claim that the nonzero vectors in $\{z_\alpha, z_\alpha T, z_\alpha T^2, \ldots\}$ form the desired basis of V.

To prove independence suppose there exist nonzero vectors r_i in the collection and nonzero scalars c_i such that $\sum_i c_i r_i = 0$. Then one of the equations $\sum_i c_i r_i = 0$, $\sum_i c_i(r_i T) = 0$, $\sum_i c_i(r_i T^2) = 0$, $\ldots$ shows that the nonzero vectors in

$$\{v_\alpha, v_\alpha T, v_\alpha T^2, \ldots\} \cap N$$

are linearly dependent, which is impossible.

Now let V' be the vector subspace of V spanned by the vectors

$$\{z_\alpha, z_\alpha T, z_\alpha T^2, \ldots\}$$

and let $z \in V$. There exists an integer $n > 0$ such that $zT^n = 0$ and there exist scalars c_{ij} such that $z = \sum_{ij} c_{ij} v_{\alpha j} T^i$. Define $r_1 = \sum_{ij} c_{ij} z_{\alpha j} T^i$. We must have $(c_{ij} v_{\alpha j} T^i) T^n = 0 = (c_{ij} z_{\alpha j} T^i) T^n$ for all i and j (why? Problem 4), and $(c_{ij} v_{\alpha j} T^i) T^{n-1}$ follows from the definition of $z_{\alpha j}$. Consequently $(z - r_1) T^{n-1} = 0$. Repeated applications of this argument show that there exist vectors $r_i \in V'$ such that $(z - \sum_i r_i) T^0 = z - \sum_i r_i = 0$. We conclude that $V = V'$ and the nonzero vectors in $\{z_\alpha, z_\alpha T, z_\alpha T^2, \ldots\}$ form a basis of V.

On the other hand observe that for every vector $u \in UT$ in this basis there is a vector $u' \in U$ in the basis satisfying $u'T = u$. By essentially the same argument employed in the proof of Theorem 1 of Lecture 3-6 it follows that the nonzero vectors in the collection $\{z_\alpha, z_\alpha T, z_\alpha T^2, \ldots\} \cap U$ form a basis of U. This completes the induction and Theorem 1 is proved.

Problems for Lecture 4—3

1. In the proof of Lemma 1 explain why there must exist basis vectors v_i such that $u_i = v_i T^{n+m}$. Explain why there exist basis vectors $u_i' \in U$ such that $u_i = u_i' T^m$.

2. In the proof of Theorem 1 show in detail that $U \cap N = (U \cap W) \oplus (UT \cap N)$.

3. In the proof of Theorem 1 show that the nonzero vectors in the set $\{z_\alpha, z_\alpha T, z_\alpha T^2, \ldots\} \cap (UT)$ form a basis of UT.

4. In the proof of Theorem 1 shown that $(c_{ij} v_{\alpha j} T^i) T^n = 0 = (c_{ij} z_{\alpha j} T^i) T^n$ and $(c_{ij} v_{\alpha j} T^i) T^{n-1} = (c_{ij} z_{\alpha j} T^i) T^{n-1}$ for all i and j.

5. In the proof of Theorem 1 show that the nonzero vectors in the collection $\{z_\alpha, z_\alpha T, z_\alpha T^2, \ldots\} \cap U$ form a basis of U.

6. If $T^2 = 0$ in Theorem 1, must U and V have a simultaneous basis under T? If dim $V = 3$ in Theorem 1, must U and V have a simultaneous basis under T?

Lecture 4–4

Algebraic Operators.   Let T be an operator on a real or complex vector space V. If V is finite-dimensional then T is annulled by its characteristic polynomial. In general, however, T need not be annulled by any nonzero polynomial as the following example illustrates.

Example 1.   Suppose V has a countably infinite basis $\{z_0, z_1, z_2, \ldots\}$ and let T be the operator for which $z_0 T = 0$, $z_n T = z_{n-1}$ for all $n > 0$. Observe that

$$z_n(a_n T^n + a_{n-1} T^{n-1} + \cdots + a_1 T + a_0)$$
$$= a_n z_0 + a_{n-1} z_1 + \cdots + a_1 z_{n-1} + a_0 z_n.$$

Clearly T is not annulled by any nonzero polynomial.

However, some operators on an infinite-dimensional vector space V are annulled by a polynomial, e.g., the scalar operators. We make the

Definition 1.   *An operator T on a real or complex vector space is said to be algebraic if there exists a nonzero polynomial p for which $p(T) = 0$ on V.*

In particular every operator on a finite-dimensional vector space is algebraic. Now suppose T is an algebraic operator on V. Let p be a monic polynomial of minimal degree that annuls T, say, $p(x) = x^n + a_{n-1}x^{n-1} + a_{n-2}x^{n-2} + \cdots + a_0$. Then p is the unique polynomial with these properties; for if

$$T^n + a_{n-1} T^{n-1} + \cdots + a_0 = T^n + b_{n-1} T^{n-1} + \cdots + b_0 = 0$$

then $(a_{n-1} - b_{n-1}) T^{n-1} + \cdots + (a_0 - b_0) = 0$. It follows that $a_i = b_i$ for all i; otherwise

$$T^j + (a_j - b_j)^{-1}(a_{j-1} - b_{j+1}) T^{j-1} + \cdots + (a_j - b_j)^{-1}(a_0 - b_0) = 0$$

where j is the largest index for which $a_j \neq b_j$, contrary to the assumption that the degree of p is minimal for monic polynomials which annul T. We make the

Definition 2.   *Let T be an algebraic operator on a real or complex vector space V. The minimum polynomial of T is the (unique) monic polynomial of minimal degree that annuls T.*

Now let T be algebraic on V and let $p(x) = x^n + a_{n-1}x^{n-1} + \cdots + a_0$ be the minimum polynomial of T. In the vector space of all operators on V the vectors $1, T, T^2, \ldots, T^{n-1}$ are linearly independent. Why? (Problem 1.) Let M be the vector subspace for which $1, T, \ldots, T^{n-1}$ constitute a basis.

Suppose $S \in M$ and $S = \sum_{i=0}^{n-1} b_i T^i$. Then

$$ST = \sum_{i=0}^{n-1} b_i T^{i+1} = b_{n-1}T^n + \sum_{i=0}^{n-2} b_i T^{i+1}$$
$$= -\sum_{i=0}^{n-1} b_{n-1}a_i T^i + \sum_{i=0}^{n-2} b_i T^{i+1} \in M.$$

By induction on m the reader can easily prove that $T^m \in M$ for all indices $m = 1, 2, 3, \ldots$. Thus M is the algebra of all polynomials in T on V, and the dimension of the vector subspace M of the vector space of all operators on V is the degree of the minimum polynomial of T. Note that if $z \in V$, then dim zM cannot exceed the degree of the minimum polynomial of T. Why? (Problem 2.)

Let T now be an operator on a real vector space V, let $V + iV$ be the complexification of V and let T' be the operator on the complex vector space $V + iV$ induced by T. If p is a polynomial with real coefficients, then $Vp(T') \subset V$, and $(iV)p(T') \subset iV$. It follows that if p is a polynomial with real coefficients for which $p(T) = 0$ on V, then $p(T') = 0$ on $V + iV$. And if $\sum_j (a_j + ib_j)(T')^j = 0$ on $V + iV$, where the a_j and b_j are real, then $\sum_j a_j T^j = \sum_j b_j T^j = 0$ on V. We conclude then that T is algebraic on V iff T' is algebraic on $V + iV$; and if T and T' are algebraic then they have the same minimum polynomial which, of course, must have real coefficients.

We present now

Theorem 1. *Let T be an operator on a real or complex vector space V. Then the following are equivalent.*
(1)   *T is algebraic on V,*
(2)   *$\sup_{z \in V} (\dim zM) < \infty$ where M is the operator algebra of all polynomials in T.*

PROOF. Assume (1). Then $\sup_{z \in V} (\dim zM)$ cannot exceed the degree of the minimum polynomial of T. Hence (1) $\Rightarrow$ (2). Now assume (2). It suffices to prove (1) for complex scalars; for if T satisfies (2) on a real vector space V then T' satisfies (2) on the complexification $V + iV$ of V, T' is algebraic on $V + iV$, and T is algebraic on V. Hence we assume V is complex.

For each scalar c let V_c denote the subspace of V composed of all vectors annihilated by powers of the operator $T - c$. For each $z \in V$, let $n(z)$ denote dim zM. By (2), $n(z) < \infty$, and the vectors $z, zT, zT^2, \ldots, zT^{n(z)}$ are linearly dependent. Say $0 = \sum_{i=0}^{n(z)} a_i z T^i$ where not all the $a_i = 0$. Then z is annihilated by a polynomial in T of degree $\leq n(z)$.

We claim that V is spanned by the subspaces V_c together. To prove this let V' be the span of all the V_c. We show that any vector

$z \in V$ is in V' by induction on $n(z)$. If $n(z) = 1$, clearly there is a scalar c for which $z(T - c) = 0$ and $z \in V_c \subset V'$. Now assume that $v \in V'$ if $n(v) < N$ and set $n(z) = N$. Then z is annihilated by a polynomial p in T of degree N. Say $p(x) = (x - c_1)(x - c_2) \cdots (x - c_N)$, and $z(T - c_1)(T - c_2) \cdots (T - c_N) = 0$. Either all the scalars c_i coincide or else two or more are distinct. In the former case $z \in V_c \subset V'$ where $c_i = c$ for each i; in the latter case suppose $c_i \neq c_j$ for $i \neq j$. Then $z(T - c_i)$ and $z(T - c_j) \in V'$ by the inductive hypothesis and $z = z[(T - c_i) - (T - c_j)](c_j - c_i)^{-1} \in V'$. This completes the induction and $V = V'$.

We claim that the subspaces V_c are linearly independent. The proof is by contradiction. Suppose $0 \neq z \in V_c$ and $z = \sum z_i$ where $z_i \in V_{c_i}$ and $c_i \neq c$ for each i. Say n is an integer for which $z_i(T - c_i)^n = 0$ for each i. We can suppose $z \neq 0$ and $z(T - c) = 0$ by replacing z with $z(T - c)^e$, and replacing z_i with $z_i(T - c)^e$ for an appropriate integer e if necessary. Then $z(T - c_1) = z(T - c) + (c - c_1)z = (c - c_1)z$; and repeated applications of this principle show that

$$\prod_i (c - c_i)^n z = z \prod_i (T - c_i)^n = \sum_j z_j \prod_i (T - c_i)^n = 0,$$

which is impossible.

Hence V is the direct sum of all the V_c. We claim that for any scalar c, $V_c(T - c)^n = (0)$ where $n = \sup_{z \in V} (\dim zM)$. The proof is by contradiction; if $z \in V_c$ and $z(T - c)^n \neq 0$ then the vectors $z, z(T - c), z(T - c)^2, \ldots, z(T - c)^n$ are linearly independent by Problem 9' of Lecture 3-4, contrary to the definition of n.

We claim that there are at most finitely many distinct scalars c for which $V_c \neq (0)$. The proof is by contradiction; let $n = \sup_{z \in V} (\dim zM)$ and suppose $V_{c_0}, V_{c_1}, \ldots, V_{c_n} \neq (0)$ where the c_i are distinct. Set $z = \sum_{i=0}^n z_i$ where $z_i \neq 0$ and $z_i(T - c_i) = 0$. By a previous argument we have for each index i, $z \prod_{j \neq i} (T - c_j) = z_i \prod_{j \neq i} (T - c_j) = \prod_{j \neq i} (c_i - c_j)z_i$ and $z_i \in zM$. It follows that zM contains the linearly independent vectors $z_0, \ldots, z_n$ and $\dim zM > n$, contrary to the definition of n. Thus there can exist at most finitely many distinct scalars c for which $V_c \neq (0)$. (Indeed at most n such scalars.) Finally V is the direct sum of the subspaces $V_{c_1}, \ldots, V_{c_m}$, say, and $V \prod_{j=1}^m (T - c_j)^n = (0)$. Thus T is annulled by $\prod_{j=1}^m (x - c_j)^n$ and (2) $\Rightarrow$ (1).

If T is algebraic on V we saw that $\dim zM \leq$ degree of the minimum polynomial of T for all $z \in V$. We show that there exist $z \in V$ for which equality holds. (See also Problem 11.)

Theorem 2. *Let T be an algebraic operator on a complex vector space V. Then there exists a $z \in V$ for which $\dim zM =$ the degree of the minimum polynomial of T.*

PROOF. By the proof of Theorem 1, V is the direct sum of subspaces V_c which are invariant under the operator $T - c$, and $T - c$ is nilpotent on V_c of index q_c, say. Also V_c is nonzero for at most finitely many scalars c. In each nonzero V_c select a vector z_c for which $z_c(T - c)^{q_c-1} \neq 0$, and set $z = \sum_c z_c$. Since M contains the projection with range V_c that annihilates all the subspaces V_d, $d \neq c$ (see Theorem 2 of Lecture 3-5) it is clear that zM contains the vectors z_c, $z_c(T - c)$, $z_c(T - c)^2$, ..., $z_c(T - c)^{q_c-1}$ and $\dim zM \geq \sum_c q_c$. But T is annulled by the polynomial $\prod_c (x - c)^{q_c}$, which has degree $\sum_c q_c$. It follows that $\dim zM = \sum_c q_c$ and that $\prod_c (x - c)^{q_c}$ is the minimum polynomial of T.

Problems for Lecture 4—4

1. If the degree of the minimum polynomial of an algebraic operator T is n, why are the operators $1, T, T^2, \ldots, T^{n-1}$ linearly independent in the vector space of all operators on V?

2. Show by induction on m that $T^m \in M$ for any algebraic operator T where M is the operator algebra defined as before.

3. If T is an algebraic operator and if $z \in V$ show that $\dim zM$ cannot exceed the degree of the minimum polynomial of T.

4. In the proof of Theorem 1 show why T' satisfies (2) on $V + iV$ iff T satisfies (2) on V. Show why T is algebraic on V iff T' is algebraic on $V + iV$.

5. In the proof of Theorem 2 explain why the projections mentioned lie in M.

6. If T is algebraic on V show that for any polynomial p, $p(T)$ is also algebraic on V. (Hint: the vector space spanned by all the powers of T on V is finite-dimensional.)

7. If V is a real or complex vector space in the proof of Theorem 1, explain why T must satisfy (2) on V iff T^2 satisfies (2) on V.

8. In the proof of Theorem 2 explain in detail why zM contains the vectors z_c, $z_c(T - c)$, ..., $z_c(T - c)^{q_c-1}$.

9. Suppose S is algebraic and $ST = 1$ (or $TS = 1$) on a vector space V. Prove that T equals a polynomial in S and that T is the inverse of S. (Hint: let p be the minimum polynomial of S and consider $p(S)T$ or $Tp(S)$.)

10. Prove that if S is an algebraic operator mapping V onto V, then S has null space (0) and is invertible. Prove that if S is an algebraic operator with null space (0), then S maps V

onto V and is invertible. (Hint: use the minimum poly-nomial of S and apply Problem 9.)

11. Let T be an algebraic operator on V. For any $z \in V$ show that there exists a unique monic polynomial p of lowest degree such that $zp(T) = 0$. We call p the minimum polynomial of z. Prove

    (a) If p is the minimum polynomial of z and if $zq(T) = 0$, then p divides q. (Hint: use the Euclidean algorithm.)

    (b) If $z_1, \ldots, z_n \in V$ have minimum polynomials $p_1, \ldots, p_n$, respectively, no two of which have a common divisor of positive degree, then the minimum poly-nomial of $z = \sum z_i$ is $p_1 p_2 \ldots p_n$. (Hint: let p be the minimum polynomial of z and prove that $z_i p(T) p_2(T) p_3(T) \cdots p_n(T) = 0$ for each i, p_1 divides $p p_2 p_3 \cdots p_n$, and p_1 divides p by Lecture 1-2. Similarly p_i divides p for each i and, hence, $p_1 p_2 \cdots p_n$ divides p by Theorem 3 of Lecture 1-2.)

    (c) Use polynomials to prove Theorem 2 in both the real and complex cases as follows. Let $p_1^{k_1} p_2^{k_2} \cdots p_n^{k_n}$ be the minimum polynomial of T where the p_i are the distinct irreducible factors. Show that there exists a $z \in V$ such that $zp_1^{k_1-1}(T) p_2^{k_2}(T) \cdots p_n^{k_n}(T) \neq 0$ and the minimum polynomial of $v_1 = zp_2^{k_2}(T) p_3^{k_3}(T) \cdots p_n^{k_n}(T)$ is $p_1^{k_1}$. Similarly for each index i there is a $v_i \in V$ with minimum polynomial $p_i^{k_i}$.

    (d) In (c) let V_i be the null space of the operator $p_i^{k_i}(T)$. Let $S_i = \prod_{j \neq i} p_j^{k_j}(T)$. Show that there exists a polynomial q_i such that $q_i(S_i)S_i$ is the projection with range V_i that annihilates all the V_j, $j \neq i$. (Hint: use the approach in the proof of Theorem 2 of Lecture 3-5.)

    (e) Use (d) to show that the subspaces V_i form a direct sum $W = V_1 \oplus V_2 \oplus \cdots \oplus V_n$.

    (f) Prove that $V = V_1 \oplus \cdots \oplus V_n$. (Hint: assume $V \neq W$ and let T' be the operator induced by T on the quotient space V/W. Then the minimum poly-nomial of T' divides $p_1^{k_1} p_2^{k_2} \cdots p_n^{k_n}$ and there exists a vector $z \in V - W$ such that $(z + W) p_i(T') = W$ for some i. But $z \prod_{j \neq i} p_j^{k_j}(T) \in V_i$ which is impossible. Why?)

12. Use Problem 11 to provide another proof of Theorem 1 in the real and complex cases. (Hint: if T is not algebraic on V then we can construct a finite-dimensional subspace U of V

invariant under T such that the degree of the minimum polynomial of T on U exceeds $\sup_{z \in U} \dim zM$.)

13. Let W be a subspace of V invariant under an operator T on V, and suppose for each $z \in V$ there is a nonzero polynomial p satisfying $zp(T) = 0$. We use the term "mip" as in Problem 13 of Lecture 3-5.

(a) Given $z \in V - W$ and a mip p with $zp(T) \in W$, prove that $zq(T) \notin W$ if q is the product of mip's different from p. (Hint: first let q be a mip different from p and use the Euclidean algorithm.)

(b) For each mip p let V_p denote the union of the null spaces of $p^n(T)$, $n = 1, 2, \ldots$. Prove that the nonzero V_p are linearly independent. (Hint: if $z \neq 0$, $zp(T) = 0$, and z is in the span of all the V_q, $q \neq p$, then we can find a product r of mip's different from p such that $zr(T) = 0$. Now set $W = (0)$ in (a).)

(c) Prove that V is the direct sum of the nonzero V_p. (Hint: let W be the span of all the V_p and suppose $W \neq V$. Select $z \in V - W$ and a monic polynomial p satisfying $zp(T) \in W$ such that there exist no $y \in V - W$ and polynomial q with $yq(T) \in W$ and $\deg q < \deg p$. Now if $p = p_1 p_2$, $0 < \deg p_2 < \deg p$, then p_2 and $zp_1(T) \in V - W$ would conflict with our choice of z and p. Hence p is a mip. Since $zp(T) \in W$ show that there exists a product q of mip's different from p such that $zq(T) \in V_p \subset W$, contrary to (a).)

Note that in Problem 13 we did not use dimensions of subspaces, greatest common divisors of polynomials, or the fact that a polynomial is the product of irreducible factors.

$\mathcal{L}$ecture 4–5

Subspaces Invariant Under Nilpotent Operators. In Lecture 4-2 we discussed subspaces of a vector space invariant under an operator algebra. In the present lecture we discuss subspaces invariant under a nilpotent operator, and more generally, under an algebraic operator. In particular, if U is a subspace invariant under the nilpotent operator T we shall determine necessary and sufficient conditions for the existence of a subspace W complementary to U and invariant under T. The following example shows that such a subspace W need not exist.

Example 1. Let V be a 4-dimensional vector space over the real or complex field and let $\{z_1, z_2, z_3, z_4\}$ be a linear basis of V. Let U be the subspace spanned by z_1 and z_2 and let T be the operator for which $z_2 = z_1 T$, $z_2 T = 0$, $z_3 = z_4 T$, $z_2 = z_3 T$. Plainly $T^3 = 0$ on V, $UT \subset U$ and T is nilpotent on U. We claim there exists no subspace W invariant under T which is complementary to U. The proof is by contradiction; suppose such a subspace W exists. Because U and W span V it follows that W contains a vector $z = a_1 z_1 + a_2 z_2 + a_3 z_3 + a_4 z_4$ where the a_i are scalars with $a_4 \neq 0$. Hence $zT^2 = a_4 z_2$ is a nonzero vector in $W \cap U$ contrary to the assumption that W and U are complementary.

We present the

Theorem 1. *Let T be an operator on a real or complex vector space V and let U be a subspace invariant under T on which T is nilpotent. Then there exists a subspace W of V complementary to U and also invariant under T iff $UT^n = U \cap (VT^n)$ for all integers $n > 0$.*

Before developing a proof we observe that the condition $UT^n = U \cap (VT^n)$ cannot be replaced by $UT = U \cap (VT)$ alone in Theorem 1 as can be seen readily from Example 1.

PROOF. It is evident that the existence of W implies $UT^n = U \cap (VT^n)$. Indeed, if z is any vector in V and $zT^n \in U$ then $z = u + w$ where $w \in W$, $u \in U$, $zT^n = uT^n + wT^n$; it follows that $uT^n \in U$, $wT^n \in U \cap W$, $wT^n = 0$, and $zT^n = uT^n \in U$. Consequently $UT^n = U \cap (VT^n)$ for all integers $n > 0$.

Now assume $UT^n = U \cap (VT^n)$ for all integers $n > 0$. Let q be the index of nilpotence of T on U; the proof is by induction on q. If $q = 1$ then $(0) = UT = U \cap (VT)$. Let W be any subspace complementary to U which contains VT; then $WT \subset VT \subset W$.

Assume the conclusion for index $q - 1$. Then UT is a subspace of VT and UT is invariant under the contraction of T to VT. Furthermore the contraction of T to VT is nilpotent on UT with index $q - 1$. Why? (Problem 1.) Also for any integer $n > 0$

$$(UT) \cap [(VT)T^n] \subset U \cap (VT^{n+1}) = UT^{n+1} = (UT)T^n$$

and by the inductive hypothesis there exists a subspace W_0 invariant under T for which $VT = W_0 \oplus (UT)$. It follows that

$$U \cap W_0 = U \cap [W_0 \cap (VT)] = [U \cap (VT)] \cap W_0$$
$$= (UT) \cap W_0 = (0).$$

Let W_1 be the subspace composed of all vectors $W \in V$ for which $wT \in W_0$. Then $W_0 \cap (U \cap W_1) \subset W_0 \cap U = (0)$ and $W_0 \cap (U \cap W_1) = (0)$. Now W_0, $U \cap W_1$ and $W_0 \oplus (U \cap W_1)$ are subspaces of W_1; let W_2 be any subspace for which $W_1 = W_2 \oplus W_0 \oplus (U \cap W_1)$ and put $W = W_2 \oplus W_0$.

We claim that W has the desired properties. Clearly $WT \subset W_1 T \subset W_0 \subset W$ because $W \subset W_1$; also $W \cap (U \cap W_1) = (0)$ and $U \cap W = U \cap (W_1 \cap W) = (U \cap W_1) \cap W = (0)$. Now let $v \in V$. Then $vT = x + w$ for some $x \in UT$ and some $w \in W_0$; hence there is a vector $u \in U$ for which $vT = uT + w$, $w = (v - u)T$, and the vector $v - u \in W_1$. Then $v = u + (v - u)$ and it follows that U and W_1 together span V. But $W_2 \oplus W_0$, $U \cap W_1$, and W_1 and U are subspaces of $U \oplus W$. Finally $V = U \oplus W$ and W is invariant under T. This completes the proof.

Corollary 1. *Let T be an operator on a vector space V and let $\{U_\alpha\}$ be a nest of subspaces invariant under T, such that T is nilpotent on their span U, and such that for each index α there exists a subspace W_α invariant under T and complementary to U_α. Then there exists a subspace W invariant under T and complementary to U.*

PROOF. Clearly T is nilpotent on each U_α. Let z be a vector in V for which $zT^n \in U$; then $zT^n \in U_\alpha$ for some index α and $zT^n \in U_\alpha T^n \subset UT^n$. Then $U \cap (VT^n) \subset UT^n$ and the conclusion is evident from Theorem 1.

Corollary 2. *Let U be a subspace of V that is invariant under T such that T is nilpotent on U. Let $\{V_\alpha\}$ be a nest of subspaces containing U and invariant under T such that for each index α there is a subspace W_α invariant under T for which $V_\alpha = W_\alpha \oplus U$. Then there exists a subspace W invariant under T for which the span of all the V_α is $W \oplus U$.*

PROOF. Let V' be the span of all the V_α and let z be a vector in V' for which $zT^n \in U$. Then $z \in V_\alpha$ for some index α and $zT^n \in UT^n$. Hence $U \cap (V'T^n) \subset UT^n$ and the proof is complete.

Corollary 3. *Let T be a nilpotent operator on a vector space V with index of nilpotence q and let z be a vector for which $zT^{q-1} \neq 0$. Then there is a subspace W invariant under T and complementary to the subspace spanned by the vectors z, zT, zT^2, ..., and zT^{q-1}.*

PROOF. Suppose $v \in V$ and n is some positive integer $<q$ such that zT^n is a nonzero vector in the subspace U spanned by the vectors z, zT, zT^2, ..., zT^{q-1}. Let $vT^n = \sum_{i=0}^{q-1} c_i z T^i$ where the c_i are scalars and j is the least index k for which $c_k \neq 0$. (We do not exclude the possibility that $j = 0$.) Now

$$(vT^n)\,T^{q-j-1} = vT^{q+n-j-1} = \sum_{i=j}^{q-1} c_i z T^{q+i-j-1} = c_j z T^{q-1} \neq 0$$

because $c_j \neq 0$ and $zT^{q-1} \neq 0$. Hence $q + n - j - 1 \leq q - 1$ and $n \leq j$. Consequently $(\sum_{i=j}^{q-1} c_i z T^{i-n})\,T^n = \sum_{i=j}^{q-1} c_i z T^i = vT^n$ and $vT^n \in UT^n$. Hence $UT^n = U \cap (VT^n)$ and the conclusion follows.

We now turn to algebraic operators on a complex vector space.

Corollary 4. *Let T be an algebraic operator on a complex vector space V and let U be a subspace invariant under T. Then there exists a subspace W complementary to U and invariant under T iff $U(T - c)^n = U \cap [V(T - c)^n]$ for every integer $n > 0$ and every eigenvalue c of T.*

PROOF. Let V_c be the subspace composed of all vectors annihilated by powers of the operator $T - c$. Then V_c and $U \cap V_c$ are invariant under T and the conclusion follows from Theorem 1. How? (Problem 4.)

We consider now the algebra of all polynomials in T on V.

Theorem 2. *Let T be an algebraic operator on a complex vector space V and let M be the operator algebra composed of all polynomials in T. Then M is completely reducible iff the operators $T - c$ and $(T - c)^2$ have the same null space for every eigenvalue c of T.*

PROOF. If $T - c$ and $(T - c)^2$ have the same null space then it follows (Lecture 4-4) that V is the direct sum of subspaces V_c, such that the contraction of T to V_c is the scalar operator c. Thus if U is a subspace invariant under M, $U \cap V_c$ is invariant under T and it is clear that there exists a subspace W complementary to U and invariant under M. Why? (Problem 6.) Furthermore the null space of M is (0) because $1 \in M$, and hence M is completely reducible.

Now assume M is completely reducible. Then there cannot exist a vector z in the null space of $(T - c)^2$ but not in the null space of $T - c$; for otherwise we have $z(T - c) \in U$, where U is the null space of $T - c$, and $z(T - c) \notin U(T - c)$. Then by Theorem 1, M is not completely reducible.

We remark that in Theorem 2, M is irreducible iff V has dimension 1; for if M is irreducible then the null space of $T - c$ must be V for an eigenvalue c, and this space has dimension at most 1. Explain (Problem 7).

In conclusion we present an example demonstrating that Theorem 1 is no longer valid if we drop the hypothesis that T is nilpotent on U.

Example 2. Let V be a real or complex vector space with a countably infinite basis composed of the vectors $z_0, z_1, z_2, \ldots, z_n, \ldots, v_{11}, v_{21}, v_{22}, v_{31}, v_{32}, v_{33}, \ldots, v_{n1}, v_{n2}, v_{n3}, \ldots, v_{nn}, \ldots$. Let T be the operator for which $z_0 T = 0$, $z_n T = z_{n-1}$ for $n > 0$, $v_{n1} T = z_0$ for all n, and $v_{nj} T = v_{n,j-1}$ for all $j > 1$ and all n. Note that T is not nilpotent on V, though each vector in V is annihilated by some power of T (Problem 11). Let U be the subspace of V spanned by the vectors z_0 and v_{ij}. Then U is invariant under T.

For any integer $n > 0$, if $\left(a_0 z_0 + \sum_{i=1}^m a_i z_i + \sum_{i,j=1}^m b_{ij} v_{ij}\right) T^n \in U$ then

$$\left(\sum_{i=1}^m a_i v_{m+1,i} + \sum_{i,j=1}^m b_{ij} v_{ij}\right) T^n$$
$$= \left(a_0 z_0 + \sum_{i=1}^m a_i z_i + \sum_{i,j=1}^m b_{ij} v_{ij}\right) T^n.$$

Explain (Problem 8). Thus $UT^n = U \cap (VT^n)$ for all $n > 0$.

We claim that there exists no subspace W of V complementary to U and invariant under T. The proof is by contradiction; suppose such a subspace W exists. Let $z_1 = w + u$ where $w \in W$ and $u \in U$. Say $u = az_0 + \sum_{i,j=1}^m b_{ij} v_{ij}$. Now let $z_{m+1} = w' + u'$ where $w' \in W$ and $u' \in U$. Then $w + u = w' T^m + u' T^m$ and consequently $u' T^m = u$. Furthermore $\sum_{i,j=1}^m b_{ij} v_{ij} \neq 0$; for otherwise $wT = z_0 \in U \cap W$ which is not possible. It follows that $u' T^m = \sum_{i,j=1}^m b_{ij} v_{ij} + az_0$. But clearly this is not possible (Problem 9). Consequently no such subspace W exists.

Problems for Lecture 4—5

1. In the proof of Theorem 1 why is T nilpotent on UT with index $q - 1$?
2. In the proof of Theorem 1 why is the set W_1 composed of all vectors $w \in V$ for which $wT \in W_0$ a subspace of V?
3. In the proof of Theorem 1 why does $W_0 \cap (U \cap W_1) = (0)$?
4. In the proof of Corollary 4 show how Theorem 1 applies.
5. In the proof of Theorem 2 show why the contraction of T to V_c is the scalar operator c on V_c when $T - c$ and $(T - c)^2$ have the same null space.
6. In the proof of Theorem 2 explain why there exists a subspace W complementary to U and invariant under M.
7. If M is irreducible in the proof of Theorem 2, explain why $\dim V = 1$.

8. In Example 2 explain why

$$\left(a_0 z_0 + \sum_{i=1}^{m} a_i z_i + \sum_{i,j=1}^{m} b_{ij} v_{ij}\right) T^n \in U$$

implies

$$\left(\sum_{i=1}^{m} a_i v_{m+1,i} + \sum_{i,j=1}^{m} b_{ij} v_{ij}\right) T^n$$
$$= \left(a_0 z_0 + \sum_{i=1}^{m} a_i z_i + \sum_{i,j=1}^{m} b_{ij} v_{ij}\right) T^n.$$

9. In Example 2 explain why there exists no $z \in V$ satisfying $z T^m = \sum_{i,j=1}^{m} b_{ij} v_{ij} + a z_0$.

10. Let T be nilpotent on V, let N be the null space of T, and suppose U is a subspace of N. Prove that there exist complementary subspaces V_1 and V_2, invariant under T, such that $U = V_1 \cap N$. (Hint: use the same approach employed in Lecture 3-6.)

11. Let T be an operator on a vector space V. We say that T is locally nilpotent if for each $z \in V$, there exists an integer n with $z T^n = 0$. Show that the operator T in Example 2 is locally nilpotent. Can such an operator by algebraic? Why?

12. Let T be locally nilpotent on V, let N be the null space of T, and suppose W is a subspace of V containing N. Assume further that $W T^n = W \cap (V T^n)$ for each n. Prove $W = V$. (Hint: given $z \in V$ show that $z \in W$ by employing induction on the smallest integer q satisfying $z T^q = 0$.)

13. Let T be locally nilpotent on V and let N be the null space of T. Prove that there exist vectors z_α such that the nonzero vectors in the collection $\{z_\alpha, z_\alpha T, z_\alpha T^2, \ldots\}$ constitute a basis of V iff N is the union of an ascending sequence of subspaces $U_1 \subset U_2 \subset U_3 \subset \cdots$ such that $(V T^n) \cap U_n = (0)$ for each index n. (Hint: if the required basis exists it will be easy to construct the subspaces U_n. Assume that the U_n exist as stated, and let N_n be the null space of T^n for each n. Use Problem 10 to show the existence of subspaces $S_1, S_2, S_3, \ldots, R_1, R_2, R_3, \ldots$, invariant under T and satisfying $S_n \cap N = U_n$ and $N_n = R_n \oplus S_n$. Now use induction to show the existence of subspaces S_n' and R_n' satisfying $S_n' \cap N = U_n$, $N_n = R_n' \oplus S_n'$, and $S_1' \subset S_2' \subset S_3' \subset \cdots$. Then it follows from Problem 12 that the union of all the S_n' is V.)

14. Construct a 2-dimensional vector space V, a subspace U of V, and a nilpotent operator on V illustrating the same principle as Example 1.

15. If $U T = U \cap (V T)$ and $\dim V = 3$ in Theorem 1, must there exist a subspace W, invariant under T, and complementary to U?

$\mathcal{L}$ecture 4–6

Operators Commuting with Algebraic Operators. If T is an operator on a vector space V any operator that commutes with T also commutes with any polynomial in T. It is natural to ask the converse question. If S is an operator commuting with every operator that commutes with T, must S coincide with some polynomial in T? This is not in general true as is demonstrated by the

Example. Let V have a countably infinite basis $\{z_n\}$ where n runs over all the integers, positive, negative, and 0. Let T be the operator for which $z_n T = z_{n+1}$ for all n, and let S be the operator for which $z_n S = z_{n-1}$ for all n. Then ST and TS are both the identity operator on V. If A is an operator for which $AT = TA$, we have $AS = STAS = SATS = SA$. But obviously there is no polynomial p for which $z_0 = z_1 p(T)$ and S does not coincide with any polynomial in T.

In this lecture we show that the only operators on a complex vector space that commute with all the operators commuting with a given algebraic operator T are polynomials in T. We begin with

Lemma 1. *Let T be a nilpotent operator on V and suppose the nonzero vectors $z, zT, zT^2, \ldots, zT^{n-1}$ constitute a basis of V. Let S be an operator commuting with T. Then there is a unique polynomial p of degree $<n$ such that $S = p(T)$.*

PROOF. From the basis of V we see that there cannot exist a nonzero polynomial q of degree less than n such that $q(T) = 0$ (Problem 2). Hence there is at most one polynomial p of degree less than n with $S = p(T)$ (Problem 3).

From the given basis of V it is clear that for any $v \in V$ there is a polynomial q such that $v = zq(T)$. In particular let $zS = zp(T)$. If $v = zq(T)$ we have $vS = zq(T)S = zSq(T) = zp(T)q(T) = zq(T)p(T) = vp(T)$ and $S = p(T)$ on V.

Lemma 2. *Let T be a nilpotent operator of index n on V and suppose the nonzero vectors $z, zT, \ldots, zT^{n-1}, w, wT, \ldots, wT^{m-1}$ constitute a basis of V where $zT^n = wT^m = 0$. Let S be an operator commuting with every operator that commutes with T. Then there is a unique polynomial p of degree less than n such that $S = p(T)$.*

PROOF. Because n is the index of nilpotence of T, $m \leq n$. Let W be the subspace spanned by the vectors $w, wT, \ldots, wT^{m-1}$, Z be the subspace spanned by $z, zT, \ldots, zT^{n-1}$, Z_1 be the subspace spanned by zT^{n-m}, zT^{n-m+1}, ..., zT^{n-1}, and let U be the subspace spanned by $w + zT^{n-m}$, $(w + zT^{n-m})T$, ..., $(w + zT^{n-m})T^{m-1}$. The projection with null space Z and range U commutes with T because Z and U are invariant under T. Then this projection also commutes with S, and Z and U are invariant under S. By a similar argument W is invariant under S. It follows from this that Z_1 is invariant under S. Explain (Problem 5).

Let $[s_{ij}]$ be the matrix of the contraction of S to W relative to the ordered basis w, wT, ..., wT^{m-1}, and let $[s_{ij}]$ be the matrix of the contraction of S to Z_1 relative to the ordered basis zT^{n-m}, zT^{n-m+1}, ..., zT^{n-1}. Since U is invariant under S it follows that $s_{ij} = s_{ij}'$. (Note that $(w + zT^{n-m})S = \sum_j a_j(wT^j + zT^{n-m+j}) = \sum_j a_j wT^j + \sum_j a_j T^{n-m+j}$ and $s_{1j} = s_{1j}' = a_j$, and so forth.)

If follows from Lemma 1 that there is a unique polynomial p of degree less than n such that $S = p(T)$ on Z. Why does Lemma 1 apply here? (Problem 7.) Because $[s_{ij}] = [s_{ij}']$ we have that $S = p(T)$ also on W and on $V = W \oplus Z$.

Lemma 3.   *Let T be a nilpotent operator of index n on V and let S be an operator commuting with every operator that commutes with T. Then there is a unique polynomial p of degree less than n such that $S = p(T)$.*

PROOF.   By Lecture 3-6 there exist vectors z_α such that the nonzero vectors in the collection $\{z_\alpha, z_\alpha T, \ldots, z_\alpha T^{n-1}\}$ constitute a basis of V. Let α_0 be an index for which $z_{\alpha_0} T^{n-1} \neq 0$. Select any other index α and let V_α denote the subspace spanned by the vectors z_α, $z_\alpha T$, $z_\alpha T^2$, ..., z_{α_0}, $z_{\alpha_0} T$, $z_{\alpha_0} T^2$, ... There is a projection with range V_α that commutes with T, and consequently V_α is invariant under S. What projection? (Problem 8.) By Lemma 2 there is a unique polynomial of degree $<n$ such that $S = p(T)$ on V_α. Why does Lemma 2 apply here? (Problem 8.) Because α was arbitrary it follows that $S = p(T)$ on V.

Theorem 1.   *Let T be an algebraic operator on a complex vector space V and let S be an operator on V commuting with every operator that commutes with T. Then there is a polynomial p such that $S = p(T)$.*

PROOF.   By Lecture 4-4 there are distinct scalars $c_1, \ldots, c_n$ and subspaces $V_{c_1}, \ldots, V_{c_n}$ such that $V = V_{c_1} \oplus \cdots \oplus V_{c_n}$ and $T - c_i$ is nilpotent on V_{c_i} for each $i = 1, \ldots, n$. Furthermore there are polynomials p_i such that $p_i(T)$ is the projection with range V_{c_i} and null space $\sum_{j \neq i} \oplus V_{c_j}$. Since S commutes with $p_i(T)$, each V_{c_i} is invariant under S. The contraction of S to V_{c_i} commutes with every operator on V_{c_i} that commutes with the contraction of $T - c_i$ to V_{c_i}. Why? (Problem 7.) By Lemma 3 we have polynomials q_i such that $S = q_i(T)$ on V_{c_i} and $S = \sum_i p_i(T)q_i(T)$ on V.

We conclude with

Theorem 2.   *Let T be an algebraic operator on a complex vector space V. Then the polynomials in T are the only operators commuting with T iff* *there are vectors $z_1, \ldots, z_n$ and distinct scalars $c_1, \ldots, c_n$ such that some power of $T - c_i$ annihilates z_i and the nonzero vectors in the collection $\{z_i, z_i(T - c_i), z_i(T - c_i)^2, \ldots\}$ constitute a basis of V.*

PROOF. If we assume the existence of c_i and z_i as stated, then the argument can be completed as in the proof of Theorem 1, but Lemma 1 is used instead of Lemma 3.

If we make the contrary assumption, there must exist a scalar c for which there is a basis of V_c of the form

$$\{z_\alpha, z_\alpha(T - c), z_\alpha(T - c)^2, \ldots\}$$

where $\{z_\alpha\}$ is a set composed of more than one vector. Fix an index α_0. Then there exists a projection P, commuting with T, whose range is spanned by the vectors $z_{\alpha_0}, z_{\alpha_0}(T - c), z_{\alpha_0}(T - c)^2, \ldots$. (What projection?) But P cannot coincide with any polynomial in $T - c$ or in T. Why not? (Problem 10.)

Problems for Lecture 4—6

1. Explain why in the proof of Lemma 1 zT^iS is a linear combination of the vectors $zT^i, zT^{i+1}, \ldots, zT^{n-1}$.
2. In the proof of Lemma 1 explain why there is no nonzero polynomial q of degree less than n such that $zq(T) = 0$.
3. In the proof of Lemma 1 explain why p is unique.
4. In the proof of Lemma 2 explain why W is invariant under S.
5. In the proof of Lemma 2 show why $WS \subset W$ and $US \subset U$ imply $Z_1 S \subset Z_1$.
6. In the conclusion of the proof of Lemma 2 explain why $S = p(T)$ on Z implies $S = p(T)$ on W. (Hint: compare the matrices of the contractions of $p(T)$ to Z and to W.)
7. When we assert in the proof of Lemma 2 that $S = p(T)$ on Z why does Lemma 1 apply? (Hint: note that an operator on Z commuting with T can be extended to an operator on V that commutes with T on V.)
8. In the proof of Lemma 3 what projection with range V_α would suffice? Why does Lemma 2 apply here?
9. In the proof of Theorem 1 explain why the contraction of S to V_{c_i} commutes with every operator on V_{c_i} that commutes with the contraction of $T - c_i$ to V_{c_i}. (Hint: compare with Problem 7.)
10. In the proof of Theorem 2 why cannot the projection P coincide with any polynomial in $T - c$? Find a projection P enjoying the property stated here.

11. Use a complexification argument to show that Theorem 1 is valid for real scalars.

12. Let T be an operator on V, let M be the operator algebra of all polynomials in T, and suppose $V = zM$. Prove that if S commutes with T, then S is a polynomial in T. (Hint: if $zS = zp(T)$ and $v = zq(T)$, then

$$vS = zq(T)S = (zS)q(T) = zp(T)q(T)$$
$$= zq(T)p(T) = vp(T).)$$

13. Suppose T is algebraic on V and the minimum polynomial p of T is irreducible. Let U be a subspace of V invariant under T and let $z \in V$. Prove that if $U \cap (zM) \neq (0)$, then $z \in U$. (Hint: let $zq(T) \in U$, deg $q <$ deg p, where q has minimal degree among polynomials satisfying these properties. Use the Euclidean algorithm to show that q is a scalar.) Use the Maximum Principle to prove that V is the direct sum of subspaces of the form zM, for some $z \in V$.

14. Suppose T is algebraic on V with minimum polynomial p^k where p is irreducible. We say that a subspace U of V is cyclic if $U = zM$ for some $z \in V$. Prove that V is the direct sum of cyclic subspaces. (Hint: use induction on k and the trick employed in the proof of Theorem 1 of Lecture 3-6.)

15. Let T be an algebraic operator on a real or complex vector space V. Prove that V is the direct sum of cyclic subspaces. (Hint: use Problem 14 and also Problem 11 of Lecture 4-4.)

16. Use Problems 13 and 15, and Problem 11 of Lecture 4-4 to prove Theorem 1 for real and complex vector spaces.

17. Let T be algebraic on a real or complex vector space V. Prove that if V is not cyclic, then there exists a projection S commuting with T and not a polynomial in T. (Hint: let $p_1^{k_1} \cdots p_n^{k_n}$ be the minimum polynomial of T where the p_i are the irreducible factors. Then for some index i the null space U_i of $p_i^{k_i}(T)$ is not cyclic. Why? So U_i is the direct sum of more than one cyclic subspace. There exists a projection S commuting with T whose range is precisely one of these cyclic subspaces of U_i. What projection? Then S annihilates some nonzero vectors in the null space of $p_i(T)$, and not others. Hence S cannot coincide with any polynomial in T. Why not?)

18. Let T be an operator on V, let U be a subspace of V invariant under T, and suppose V is the direct sum of finite-dimensional subspaces invariant under T. Prove that U is also the direct sum of finite-dimensional subspaces invariant under T. (Hint: express U as the direct sum of cyclic finite-dimensional subspaces.)

19. Show that the only complex matrices commuting with

$$A = \begin{bmatrix} 2 & 0 & 0 & 0 \\ 0 & 0 & 1 & 0 \\ 0 & 0 & 0 & 1 \\ 0 & 1 & -3 & 3 \end{bmatrix}$$ are polynomials in A.

20. Let T be an algebraic operator on a real or complex vector space V and let M be the operator algebra composed of all polynomials in T. Prove

   (a) M is completely reducible iff each irreducible factor of the minimum polynomial of T appears only to the first power. (This generalizes Theorem 2 of Lecture 4-5.)

   (b) M is irreducible iff V is cyclic and the minimum polynomial of V is irreducible.

   (c) There exist no nonzero complementary subspaces U_1, U_2, both invariant under M iff V is cyclic and the minimum polynomial of T is a power of an irreducible polynomial.

21. Use Problem 15 to prove that if A and B are n by n matrices such that rank $p(A)$ = rank $p(B)$ for each polynomial p, then A is similar to B. Prove that any square matrix is similar to its transpose. Prove that if A and B are real matrices similar over the complex numbers, then A and B are similar over the real numbers.

$\mathcal{L}$ecture 4–7

Completely Reducible Operator Algebras. In Lecture 4-2 we discussed operator algebras that are completely reducible. In the present lecture we shall give definitions equivalent to "completely reducible," and finally we will show that the commutant of a completely reducible operator algebra on a vector space is completely reducible. For convenience we say that a subspace U of V is M-*invariant* if $UM \subset U$, and we say that an M-invariant subspace U of V is M-*irreducible* if U and (0) are the only M-invariant subspaces of U. Hence if U_1 is M-irreducible and if U_2 is M-invariant either $U_1 \cap U_2 = U_1$ or $U_1 \cap U_2 = (0)$. Why? (Problem 10.)

Lemma 1. *Let M be a completely reducible operator algebra on V and let U be an M-invariant subspace of V. Then the contradiction of M to U is completely reducible on U.*

PROOF. Let W be an M-invariant subspace of U. Since M is completely reducible on V there exists an M-invariant subspace W_1 for which $V = W_1 \oplus W$. Plainly $W \cap (U \cap W_1) = (0)$. If $z \in U$, then $z = w + w_1$ for some $w \in W$, $w_1 \in W_1$; but $w_1 \in U$ and $w_1 \in U \cap W_1$ because $z \in U$ and $w \in U$. Hence $U = W \oplus (U \cap W_1)$.

Theorem 1. *Let M be an operator algebra on a vector space V with null space (0). Then the following are equivalent.*

(1) *V is spanned by the family of all M-irreducible subspaces of V,*

(2) *V is the direct sum of a family of M-irreducible subspaces of V,*

(3) *For every M-invariant subspace $U_1 \neq V$ there exists a nonzero M-irreducible subspace U_2 such that $U_1 \cap U_2 = (0)$,*

(4) *M is completely reducible.*

PROOF. $(3) \Rightarrow (2)$. Note that if a family of subspaces of V is linearly dependent, then there exists a finite subfamily that is also linearly dependent. By the Maximum Principle we can find a (possibly void) maximal linearly independent family of nonzero M-irreducible subspaces $\{U_\alpha\}$ (Problem 1). Now assume property (3). It follows that this family is nonvoid, because (0) is M-invariant. Furthermore, $\sum_\alpha \oplus U_\alpha = V$; for otherwise there would exist an M-irreducible subspace $U \neq (0)$ such that $U \cap \sum_\alpha \oplus U_\alpha = (0)$ and the collection of subspaces $\{U\} \cup \{U_\alpha\}$ is linearly independent.

$(2) \Rightarrow (1)$. Clear.

$(1) \Rightarrow (4)$. Assume (1), and let U be an M-irreducible subspace $\neq V$. Let $\{U_\alpha\}$ be a (possibly void) maximal family of M-irreducible subspaces such that the subspaces $\{U\} \cup \{U_\alpha\}$ are linearly independent. Then $U \oplus \sum_\alpha \oplus U_\alpha = V$; for if W is any nonzero M-irreducible subspace different from all the U_α we have $W \cap [U \oplus \sum_\alpha \oplus U_\alpha] \neq (0)$ and $W \subset U \oplus \sum_\alpha \oplus U_\alpha$.

(4) $\Rightarrow$ (3). Assume that M is completely reducible and let $\{U_\alpha\}$ be the (possibly void) family of all M-irreducible subspaces of V. We will prove that $\sum_\alpha U_\alpha = V$ by contradiction; assume that $\sum_\alpha U_\alpha \neq V$ and let W be an M-invariant subspace complementary to $\sum_\alpha U_\alpha$. Then there exists no nonzero M-irreducible subspace of W.

Select a nonzero vector $z \in W$. Note that the union of a nest of M-invariant subspaces not containing z is an M-invariant subspace not containing z. By the Maximum Principle there is a maximal M-invariant subspace W_1 of W not containing z. By Lemma 1 the contraction of M to W is completely reducible on W, and hence there exists an M-invariant subspace W_2 of W such that $W = W_1 \oplus W_2$. On the other hand W_2 is not M-irreducible, and it follows that there exist nonzero M-invariant subspaces W_3 and W_4 of W_2 with $W_3 \cap W_4 = (0)$. Then $z \in W_1 \oplus W_3$ and $z \in W_1 \oplus W_4$ by the maximality of W_1. But $(W_1 \oplus W_3) \cap (W_1 \oplus W_4) = W_1$ (Problem 3) and $z \in W_1$ contrary to construction. This completes the proof.

Lemma 2. *If M is a nonzero operator algebra on V such that every nonzero operator $T \in M$ is invertible and $T^{-1} \in M$, then M is completely reducible.*

PROOF. It suffices to show that M satisfies the Property (1) of Theorem 1. Let z be a nonzero vector in V. Then zM is M-invariant; furthermore zM is M-irreducible, for if zT is a nonzero vector and $T \in M$, then $z = (zT)T^{-1} \in zM$ and $(zT)M = zM$. On the other hand $z = (zT)T^{-1}$ for any nonzero operator $T \in M$ and $z \in zM$. This completes the proof.

Lemma 3. *If M is an irreducible operator algebra on V, then every operator $T \in M'$ is invertible and M' is completely reducible.*

PROOF. Suppose M is irreducible. By Theorem 2 of Lecture 4-2 every nonzero operator $T \in M'$ is invertible. Furthermore $T^{-1} \in M'$; for if $S \in M$ we have $T^{-1}(ST)T^{-1} = T^{-1}(TS)T^{-1}$ and $T^{-1}S = ST^{-1}$. Then M' is completely reducible by Lemma 2.

Lemma 4. *Let P be a projection in M' and suppose VP is M-irreducible. Then the contraction of $PM'P$ to VP is completely reducible on VP.*

PROOF. Let M_1 be the contraction of M to the subspace VP. Then if $T \in M'$, the contraction of PTP to VP is in M_1'. On the other hand if $S \in M_1'$, the operator T on V for which $V(1 - P)T = (0)$ and $T = S$ on VP is in M' because $zTR = 0 = zRT$ for all $z \in V(1 - P)$, $R \in M$, and $zTR = zRT$ for all $z \in VP$, $R \in M$.

Clearly the contraction of $PM'P$ to VP is the commutant of M_1. The rest follows from Lemma 3.

Theorem 2.   *Let M be a completely reducible operator algebra on V. Then M' is also completely reducible.*

PROOF. By Theorem 1 there is a family of M-irreducible subspaces $\{U_\alpha\}$ such that $V = \sum_\alpha \oplus U_\alpha$. Again by Theorem 1, it will suffice to show that V is spanned by M'-irreducible subspaces. For each index α let P_α be the projection in M' with range U_α and null space $\sum_{\beta \neq \alpha} \oplus U_\beta$, and let M_α' denote the contraction of $P_\alpha M' P_\alpha$ to $U_\alpha = VP_\alpha$. Then by Lemma 4 each U_α is spanned by M_α'-irreducible subspaces. It suffices to prove that WM' is M'-irreducible for any M_α'-irreducible subspace W of U_α.

To prove this suppose $zT \neq 0$ for some $z \in W$, $T \in M'$. Then there is an index β such that $0 \neq zTP_\beta = z(P_\alpha TP_\beta)$, and $P_\alpha TP_\beta \neq 0$. Set $S = P_\alpha TP_\beta \in M'$; then the null space of S contains no nonzero vectors in U_α, and U_β is the range of S, because U_α and U_β are M-irreducible (Problem 4). Thus S maps U_α onto U_β and S is 1–1 on U_α. Let S_1 be the operator with null space $\sum_{\gamma \neq \beta} \oplus U_\gamma$ such that $SS_1 = P_\alpha$, $S_1 S = P_\beta$ (Problem 5). Then for any $R \in M$ we have $RS = SR$, and

$$S_1 R = S_1 P_\alpha R = S_1 R P_\alpha = S_1(RS)S_1$$
$$= S_1(SR)S_1 = P_\beta R S_1 = R P_\beta S_1 = RS_1$$

and $S_1 \in M'$. Thus $zTP_\beta S_1 \neq 0$, $zTP_\beta S_1 \in WM'$ and $zTP_\beta S_1 \in U_\alpha$. Since $P_\alpha TP_\beta S_1 P_\alpha$, $TP_\beta S_1 \in M'$ and $z \in W$ we have $zTP_\beta S_1 \in W$. Then $W \subset zTP_\beta S_1 M' \subset zTM'$ and $WM' = zTM'$. Hence WM' is M'-irreducible and the proof is complete.

The next results are related to the work in Part 2 which showed that any two bases of a finite-dimensional vector space have the same number of vectors. Given two bases of an arbitrary vector space we shall construct a 1–1 correspondence between them.

Lemma 5.   *Let M be an operator algebra on a vector space. V, let $\{U_\alpha\}$, $\{W_\beta\}$ be families of M-invariant subspaces of V and let U be an M-irreducible subspace of V. Suppose the families $\{U_\alpha\} \cup \{W_\beta\}$ and $\{U\} \cup \{U_\alpha\}$ are each linearly independent. Then there is a subspace W_{β_0} in $\{W_\beta\}$ such that the family $\{U\} \cup \{U_\alpha\} \cup \{W_\beta\}_{\beta \neq \beta_0}$ is linearly independent.*

PROOF. If the family $\{U\} \cup \{U_\alpha\} \cup \{W_\beta\}$ is linearly independent then any subspace in $\{W_\beta\}$ suffices for W_{β_0}, so we may assume without loss of generality that $U \cap (\sum_\alpha \oplus U_\alpha \oplus \sum_\beta \oplus W_\beta) \neq (0)$. We can select finitely many subspaces $W_{\beta_1}, \ldots, W_{\beta_m}$ in $\{W_\beta\}$ such that $U \cap (\sum_\alpha \oplus U_\alpha \oplus \sum_{i=1}^m \oplus W_{\beta_i}) \neq (0)$ and $U \cap (\sum_\alpha \oplus U_\alpha \oplus \sum_{i=1}^{m-1} \oplus W_{\beta_i}) = (0)$. How? (Problem 6.) It follows that $W_{\beta_m} \cap (U \oplus \sum_\alpha \oplus U_\alpha \oplus \sum_{i=1}^{m-1} \oplus W_{\beta_i}) \neq (0)$ (Problem 7) and $U \subset \sum_\alpha \oplus U_\alpha \oplus \sum_{i=1}^m \oplus W_{\beta_i}$. We claim that the family of subspaces

$\{U\} \cup \{U_\alpha\} \cup \{W_\beta\}_{\beta \neq \beta_m}$ is linearly independent. For otherwise $U \subset \sum_\alpha \oplus U_\alpha \oplus \sum_{\beta \neq \beta_m} \oplus W_\beta$ by the same reasoning as before and

$$(0) \neq W_{\beta_m} \cap (U \oplus \sum_\alpha \oplus U_\alpha + \sum_{\beta \neq \beta_m} \oplus W_\beta)$$
$$= W_{\beta_m} \cap (\sum_\alpha \oplus U_\alpha \oplus \sum_{\beta \neq \beta_m} \oplus W_\beta),$$

contrary to hypothesis.

Theorem 3. *Let M be a completely reducible operator algebra on V. Suppose $V = \sum_\alpha \oplus U_\alpha = \sum_\beta \oplus W_\beta$ where each U_α and each W_β is an M-irreducible subspace of V. Then there is a 1–1 correspondence between the family $\{W_\beta\}$ and a subfamily of $\{U_\alpha\}$.*

PROOF. We say that a set of ordered pairs $\{(U_\alpha, W_\beta)\}$ is *proper* if

(i)   the first member of each pair is one of the U_α

(ii)   the second member of each pair is one of the W_β

(iii) distinct pairs have different first members and different second members

(iv)   the aggregate of all first members of pairs together with all subspaces in $\{W_\beta\}$ that are not second members of pairs is linearly independent.

Plainly the void set is proper. Furthermore the union of a nest of proper sets is proper. To see that the union satisfies (iv) observe that a linearly dependent family of subsets has a finite linearly dependent subfamily. It follows from the Maximum Principle that there is a maximal proper set $\mathscr{S}$.

We claim that every subspace in $\{W_\beta\}$ is the second member of some pair in $\mathscr{S}$. For otherwise there exists a U_{α_0} that is not the first member of a pair in $\mathscr{S}$ and it follows from Lemma 5 that we can select a subspace W_{β_0} in $\{W_\beta\}$ such that if the pair $(U_{\alpha_0}, W_{\beta_0})$ is adjoined to $\mathscr{S}$, a proper subset larger than $\mathscr{S}$ is formed, which is impossible. This proves our claim. For the desired 1–1 correspondence map each W_β into the first member of the pair in $\mathscr{S}$ whose second member is W_β. This completes the proof of Theorem 3.

The reader familiar with the Schroeder-Bernstein theorem (see Kelley [10], "General Topology," or Halmos [5], "Naive Set Theory") will recognize that in Theorem 3, there must in fact be a 1–1 correspondence between the families $\{U_\alpha\}$ and $\{W_\beta\}$. Indeed if $\{u_\alpha\}$ and $\{w_\beta\}$ are two bases of an arbitrary vector space V then there is a 1–1 correspondence between the sets $\{u_\alpha\}$ and $\{w_\beta\}$. To see this let M be the operator algebra on V composed of all the scalar operators, let U_α be the 1-dimensional subspace of V spanned by the vector u_α and let W_β be the 1-dimensional subspace spanned by the vector w_β.

We close with a necessary and sufficient condition that an operator R lie in M where M is completely reducible on a finite-dimensional complex vector space V.

Theorem 4. *Let R be an operator on a finite-dimensional complex vector space V and let M be a completely reducible operator algebra on V. If every M-invariant subspace is also invariant under R, then $R \in M$.*

PROOF. Assume that every M-invariant subspace is invariant under R. Let P_α, P_β, S, and S_1 be defined as in the proof of Theorem 2 with $\alpha \neq \beta$. Then $P_\alpha S P_\beta = S$, $P_\beta S_1 P_\alpha = S_1$, $SS_1 = P_\alpha$, $S_1 S = P_\beta$. Obviously $S + S_1$ is a linear combination of the operators $\frac{1}{2}P_\alpha + \frac{1}{2}S + \frac{1}{2}S_1 + \frac{1}{2}P_\beta$ and $\frac{1}{2}P_\alpha - \frac{1}{2}S - \frac{1}{2}S_1 + \frac{1}{2}P_\beta$, which can be shown to be projections in M' by direct computation. Likewise $iS - iS_1$ is a linear combination of projections in M' (just replace S with iS and S_1 with $-iS_1$ in the preceding argument) and so also is $2S = (S + S_1) - i(iS - iS_1)$. It follows that R commutes with any projection in M' and therefore $RS = SR$. But for any $T \in M'$ we have $T = \sum_{ij} P_{\alpha_i} T P_{\alpha_j}$. By the corollary in Lecture 4-2 $P_{\alpha_i} T P_{\alpha_i}$ is a scalar multiple of P_{α_i}. Each $P_{\alpha_i} T P_{\alpha_j}$ is a linear combination of projections in M' and it follows that $RT = TR$. Hence $R \in M'' = M$.

Problems for Lecture 4—7

1. In the proof of $(3) \Rightarrow (2)$ in Theorem 1 use the Maximum Principle to show that there exists a maximal linearly independent family of nonzero M-irreducible subspaces $\{U_\alpha\}$.
2. In the proof of $(4) \Rightarrow (3)$ in Theorem 1 explain why the union of a nest of M-invariant subspaces not containing z is an M-invariant subspace not containing z.
3. In the proof of $(4) \Rightarrow (3)$ in Theorem 1 explain why $(W_1 \oplus W_3) \cap (W_1 \oplus W_4) = W_1$.
4. In the proof of Theorem 2 explain why the null space of S contains no nonzero vectors in U_α, and U_β is the range of S.
5. In the proof of Theorem 2 define the operator S_1 with null space $\sum_{\gamma \neq \beta} \oplus U_\gamma$ such that $SS_1 = P_\alpha$, $S_1 S = P_\beta$.
6. In the proof of Lemma 5 explain why there exist subspaces $W_{\beta_i}, \ldots, W_{\beta_m}$ in $\{W_\beta\}$ such that $U \cap (\sum_\alpha \oplus U_\alpha \oplus \sum_{i=1}^{m} \oplus W_{\beta_i}) \neq (0)$ and $U \cap (\sum_\alpha \oplus U_\alpha \oplus \sum_{i=1}^{m-1} \oplus W_{\beta_i}) = (0)$.
7. In the proof of Lemma 5 show why $W_{\beta_m} \cap (U \oplus \sum_\alpha \oplus U_\alpha \oplus \sum_{i=1}^{m-1} \oplus W_{\beta_i}) \neq (0)$ and $U \subset \sum_\alpha \oplus U_\alpha \oplus \sum_{i=1}^{m} \oplus W_{\beta_i}$.
8. In the proof of Theorem 4 show that $\frac{1}{2}P_\alpha + \frac{1}{2}S + \frac{1}{2}S_1 + \frac{1}{2}P_\beta$ and $\frac{1}{2}P_\alpha - \frac{1}{2}S - \frac{1}{2}S_1 + \frac{1}{2}P_\beta$ are projections.
9. In the proof of Theorem 4 show that $iS - iS_1$ is a linear combination of projections in M'.
10. Let M be an operator algebra on a vector space V. If U_1, U_2 are M-invariant subspaces of V and if U_1 is M-irreducible prove that either $U_1 \cap U_2 = U_1$ or $U_1 \cap U_2 = (0)$.

Part 5   FINITE-
DIMENSIONAL
UNITARY
SPACES

Lecture 5–1

Introduction. In Part 5 we consider only finite-dimensional complex vector spaces. We shall introduce a notion of "perpendicularity" (or "orthogonality" as it is sometimes called) into these spaces.

Definition 1. *Let V be a finite-dimensional vector space. We say that V is a unitary space if for each ordered pair of vectors x, y, there is a scalar (called the scalar product of x and y) denoted (x, y) such that*

(1) $(x, x) \geq 0$ *for all $x \in V$ and $(x, x) = 0$ only if $x = 0$,*

(2) $(ax + by, z) = a(x, z) + b(y, z)$ *for all $x, y, z \in V$ and all scalars a, b.*

(3) $(x, y) = \overline{(y, x)}$ *for all $x, y \in V$.*

We leave it to the reader to prove the simple lemma

(4) $(x, ay + bz) = \bar{a}(x, y) + \bar{b}(x, z)$ for all $x, y, z \in V$ and scalars a, b.

For $y \in V$ we have $(0, y) = (0, y) + (0, y)$ and $(0, y) = 0$. Likewise $(x, 0) = 0$ for any $x \in V$. In particular, $(0, 0) = 0$. Furthermore, if $x, y \in V$ and $y \neq 0$ then $0 \leq (x + ay, x + ay)$ where a denotes the scalar $-(x, y)(y, y)^{-1}$. We leave it to the reader to verify the inequality

(5) $|(x, y)|^2 \leq (x, x)(y, y)$. (This is known as the Schwarz Inequality.)

Indeed (5) holds for any $x, y \in V$; for if $y = 0$ both sides reduce to 0.

An example of a unitary space is complex Euclidean n-space under the scalar product $([x_1, \ldots, x_n], [y_1, \ldots, y_n]) = \sum_i x_i \bar{y}_i$. The verification of (1), (2), and (3) is left to the reader (Problem 1).

For convenience we sometimes denote $\sqrt{(x, x)}$ by $\|x\|$, which we call the *norm* of x. By (1) we have $\|x\| \geq 0$ and $= 0$ only if $x = 0$. Indeed $\|x\| = 0$ iff $x = 0$. From (5) we obtain $|(x, y)| \leq \|x\| \|y\|$ for any $x, y \in V$. The reader can show that $\|ax\| = |a| \|x\|$ for any scalar a and any $x \in V$. If $x + y \neq 0$ then

$$\|x + y\|^2 = (x, x + y) + (y, x + y) \leq \|x\| \|x + y\| + \|y\| \|x + y\|$$

and hence

(6) $\|x + y\| \leq \|x\| + \|y\|$. (This is known as the Triangle Inequality.)

But (6) holds for any $x, y \in V$; for if $x + y = 0$ then the left side is 0. From

$$(x + y, x + y) + (x - y, x - y) = (x, x) + (x, y) + (y, x) + (y, y)$$
$$+ (x, x) - (x, y) - (y, x) + (y, y)$$

we have

(7) $\|x + y\|^2 + \|x - y\|^2 = 2\|x\|^2 + 2\|y\|^2$ for all $x, y \in V$.

In the same way we can verify

(8) $\|\tfrac{1}{2}(x + y)\|^2 - \|\tfrac{1}{2}(x - y)\|^2 + i\|\tfrac{1}{2}(x + iy)\|^2 - i\|\tfrac{1}{2}(x - iy)\|^2 = (x, y)$ for all $x, y \in V$.

We say that $x \in V$ is a *unit* vector if $\|x\| = 1$. We say that x is *orthogonal* to y (written $x \perp y$) if $(x, y) = 0$. If $z \neq 0$, then $\|z\|^{-1}z$ is a unit vector.

Definition 2.   *We say that a set of vectors* $\{z_1, \ldots, z_n\}$ *is orthogonal if* $z_i \perp z_j$ *for* $i \neq j$. *We say that this set is orthonormal if it is orthogonal and each* z_i *is a unit vector.*

Lemma 1.   *Any unitary space V has an orthonormal basis.*

PROOF.   Let $\{z_1, \ldots, z_n\}$ be a basis of V. We define the vectors $x_1, \ldots, x_k, \ldots, x_n$ by induction on k as follows. Let x_1 be a scalar multiple of z_1 such that $\|x_1\| = 1$. Suppose unit vectors $x_1, \ldots, x_{k-1}$ have been chosen such that $x_i \perp x_j$ for $i \neq j$ and each x_i is a linear combination of $z_1, \ldots, z_i$. Let x_k be a unit vector which is a scalar multiple of the nonzero vector

$$z_k - (z_k, x_1)x_1 - (z_k, x_2)x_2 - \cdots - (z_k, x_{k-1})x_{k-1}.$$

Then x_k is a linear combination of $z_1, \ldots, z_k$, and x_k is orthogonal to the vectors $x_1, \ldots, x_{k-1}$. This completes the induction.

We say that z is *orthogonal* to the subspace U (denoted $z \perp U$) if z is orthogonal to every vector in U. By $U^\perp$ we mean the set of all vectors orthogonal to U. Of course $(0)^\perp = V$ and $V^\perp = (0)$.

Lemma 2.   *Let U be a proper nonzero subspace of a unitary space V. Then $U^\perp$ is a subspace of V and $V = U \oplus U^\perp$.*

PROOF.   Suppose $m = \dim U$ and $n = \dim V$; then $0 < m < n$. Let $\{x_1, \ldots, x_m, \ldots, x_n\}$ be an ordered basis of V such that $\{x_1, \ldots, x_m\}$ is an ordered basis of U. Construct the orthonormal basis $\{z_1, \ldots, z_n\}$ of V by employing the technique of the proof of Lemma 1 (so that z_i is a linear combination of $x_1, \ldots, x_i$). Then $\{z_1, \ldots, z_m\}$ is a basis of U and $z_{m+1}, \ldots, z_n \in U^\perp$. Any linear combination $\sum_{i=m+1}^n c_i z_i$ is orthogonal to each of the vectors $z_1, \ldots, z_m$ because $(\sum_{i=m+1}^n c z_i, z_j) = \sum_{i=m+1}^n c_i(z_i, z_j) = 0$ for any $j = 1, \ldots, m$. On the other hand if $x = \sum_{i=1}^n c_i z_i \in U^\perp$ then $0 = (x, z_j) = c_j$ for $j = 1, \ldots, m$. Thus the vectors in $U^\perp$ are precisely the linear combinations of the vectors $z_{m+1}, \ldots, z_n$. The conclusion is evident. We call $U^\perp$ the *orthogonal complement* of U.

Note that any orthonormal set $\{z_1, \ldots, z_m\}$ can be extended to an orthonormal basis of V. Just let $\{x_1, \ldots, x_m, \ldots, x_n\}$ be an ordered basis of V such that $x_i = z_i$ for $i = 1, \ldots, m$, and use the construction in the proof of Lemma 1. (The z_i are clearly linearly independent. Problem 14.)

From $U \subset U^{\perp\perp}$ and $V = U^{\perp} \oplus U^{\perp\perp}$ we can easily show that $U = U^{\perp\perp}$ (Problem 6).

Lemma 3. *Let $\{z_1, \ldots, z_n\}$ be an orthonormal set of vectors in the unitary space V. Then the following are equivalent.*

(a) *$\{z_1, \ldots, z_n\}$ is an orthonormal basis of V,*
(b) *for each $x \in V$, $x = \sum_i (x, z_i) z_i$,*
(c) *for each $x \in V$, $\|x\|^2 = \sum_i |(x, z_i)|^2$.*

PROOF. (a) $\Rightarrow$ (b). If (a) holds, then any vector x can be expressed as $\sum_i c_i z_i$ for appropriate scalars c_i, and for any index j, $(x, z_j) = (\sum_i c_i z_i, z_j) = c_j$.

(b) $\Rightarrow$ (c). If (b) holds, then

$$\|x\|^2 = (x, x) = (\sum_i (x, z_i) z_i, \sum_j (x, z_j) z_j)$$
$$= \sum_i (x, z_i) \overline{(x, z_i)} = \sum_i |(x, z_i)|^2.$$

(c) $\Rightarrow$ (a). If (a) does not hold, then there exists a nonzero vector x orthogonal to all the z_i and $\|x\|^2 > 0 = \sum_i |(x, z_i)|^2$, contrary to (c).

It is also clear that if $\{z_1, \ldots, z_n\}$ is an orthonormal set of vectors in V, then $\|x\|^2 \geq \sum_i |(x, z_i)|^2$ for any $x \in V$. Why? (Problem 7.) This is known as Bessel's Inequality.

Definition 3. *A scalar valued mapping f of a unitary space V is called a linear form on V if $f(ax + by) = af(x) + bf(y)$ for all $x, y \in V$ and all scalars a, b.*

One example of a linear form on V is defined by fixing a vector $z \in V$ and setting $f(x) = (x, z)$ for all $x \in V$.

Lemma 4. *Let f be a linear form on a unitary space V. Then there exists a unique vector $z \in V$ such that $f(x) = (x, z)$ for all $x \in V$. Furthermore $\|z\| = \sup_{\|x\|=1} |f(x)|$.*

PROOF. Let U be the set of all vectors annihilated by f. Then U is a subspace of V (Problem 8). We can dismiss the possibility that $U = V$; for in this event we may and must obviously set $z = 0$. Select nonzero $y \in U^{\perp}$; then $f(y) \neq 0$. Set $w = f(y)^{-1} y$; then $f(w) = f(y)^{-1} f(y) = 1$, and for any $x \in V$ we have $f(x - f(x)w) = f(x) - f(x) = 0$. For any $x \in V$ we have $x - f(x)w \in U$ and $0 = (x - f(x)w, w) = (x, w) - f(x)(w, w)$. Setting $z = (w, w)^{-1} w$ we have $f(x) = (x, z)$. Note also that $|f(x)| = |(x, z)| \leq \|x\| \|z\| = \|z\|$ if $\|x\| = 1$. But $|f(\|z\|^{-1} z)| = |(\|z\|^{-1} z, z)| = \|z\|$ and $\sup_{\|x\|=1} |f(x)| = \|z\|$ because $\|(\|z\|^{-1})z\| = \|z\|^{-1} \|z\| = 1$.

To prove uniqueness suppose z_1 is another vector for which $f(x) = (x, z_1)$ for all $v \in V$. Then $f(z - z_1) = (z - z_1, z_1) = (z - z_1, z)$ and $(z - z_1, z - z_1) = 0$. It follows that $z = z_1$ and the proof is complete.

Lemma 5. *Let T be an operator on a unitary space V. Then there exists a unique operator T^* on V (called the adjoint of T) such that $(xT, y) = (x, yT^*)$ for all $x, y \in V$.*

PROOF. Fix the vector $y \in V$ and define the linear form $f(x) = (xT, y)$ for $x \in V$. By Lemma 4 there exists a unique vector y' such that $f(x) = (x, y')$ for all $x \in V$. Define the mapping T^* of V into V such that $yT^* = y'$ for each $y \in V$. If a, b are scalars and if $y_1, y_2 \in V$, then

$$(xT, ay_1 + by_2) = \bar{a}(xT, y_1) + \bar{b}(xT, y_2)$$
$$= \bar{a}(x, y_1') + \bar{b}(x, y_2') = (x, ay_1' + by_2').$$

It follows that T^* is a linear operator and $(xT, y) = (x, yT^*)$ for all $x, y \in V$. To prove the uniqueness of T^* suppose S is another operator such that $(xT, y) = (x, yS)$ for all $x, y \in V$. In particular $(yT^* - yS, yS) = (yT^* - yS, yT^*)$, $(yT^* - yS, yT^* - yS) = 0$. Hence $yT^* = yS$ for all $y \in V$ and $S = T^*$.

We immediately draw the following conclusions about adjoints. For operators S and T on V, $(ST)^* = T^*S^*$ because $(x, yT^*S^*) = (xS, yT^*) = (xST, y)$ for $x, y \in V$. For scalars a and b we have $(aS + bT)^* = \bar{a}S^* + \bar{b}T^*$ because $(x, y(aS^* + bT^*)) = (x, ayS^*) + (x, byT^*) = \bar{a}(xS, y) + \bar{b}(xT, y) = (\bar{a}xS + \bar{b}xT, y) = (x(\bar{a}S + \bar{b}T), y)$. For any operator T on V we have $T^{**} = T$, because $(x, yT) = \overline{(yT, x)} = \overline{(y, xT^*)} = (xT^*, y)$ for $x, y \in V$.

Let T be an operator on a unitary space V and let $\{z_1, \ldots, z_n\}$ be an orthonormal basis of V. Then $\|(\Sigma a_i z_i) T\| \le \Sigma |a_i| \|z_i T\| \le n(\max_i |a_i|)(\max_i \|z_i T\|)$. If $\|\Sigma a_i z_i\| \le 1$ we have $1 \ge (\Sigma_i a_i z_i, \Sigma_i a_j z_j) = \Sigma_i a_i \bar{a}_i = \Sigma_i |a_i|^2$ and $\max_i |a_i| \le 1$. Thus $\sup_{\|z\|=1} \|zT\| < \infty$. We call the quantity $\sup_{\|z\|=1} \|zT\|$ the *norm* of T. Equivalently norm T (denoted $\|T\|$) $= \sup_{z \ne 0} \|zT\|/\|z\|$ because $\|(\|z\|^{-1})z\| = 1$. Note that for any vector $z \in V$ we have $\|zT\| \le \|z\| \|T\|$; for if $z \ne 0$ then $\|(\|z\|^{-1})z\| = 1$ and $\|(\|z\|^{-1}z) T\| \le \|T\|$.

Lemma 6. *For operators S and T on a unitary space V we have*
(a) $\|ST\| \le \|S\| \|T\|$,
(b) $\|S + T\| \le \|S\| + \|T\|$,
(c) $\|aT\| = |a| \|T\|$,
(d) $\|T\| = \|T^*\|$,
(e) $\|TT^*\| = \|T\|^2$.

PROOF. (a). If $\|z\| = 1$, then $\|zST\| \le \|zS\| \|T\| \le \|S\| \|T\|$.

(b). If $\|z\| = 1$, then $\|z(S + T)\| \le \|zS\| + \|zT\| \le \|S\| + \|T\|$.

(c). If $\|z\| = 1$, then $\|z(aT)\| = |a| \|zT\|$.

(d). If $\|z\| = 1$, and $zT^* \ne 0$, then

$$\|zT^*\| = ((\|zT^*\|^{-1})zT^*, zT^*) = ((\|zT^*\|^{-1})zT^*T, z)$$
$$\le \|(\|zT^*\|^{-1}zT^*) T\| \|z\| \le \|T\|$$

because $\|(\|zT^*\|)^{-1}zT^*\| = 1$. It follows that $\|T^*\| \le \|T\|$. Similarly $\|T\| = \|T^{**}\| \le \|T^*\|$ and $\|T\| = \|T^*\|$.

(e). If $\|z\| = 1$, then $\|zT\|^2 = (zT, zT) = (zTT^*, z) \le \|zTT^*\| \|z\| \le \|TT^*\|$. Hence $\|T\|^2 \le \|TT^*\|$. But on the other hand $\|TT^*\| \le \|T\| \|T^*\| = \|T\|^2$, and $\|T\|^2 = \|TT^*\|$.

Problems for Lecture 5—1

1. Verify (1), (2), and (3) for the scalar product we defined on complex Euclidean n-space.
2. Verify property (8) for any unitary space V.
3. Prove that $\|ax\| = |a| \|x\|$ for any unitary space V.
4. Show in detail why $V^\perp = (0)$ and $(0)^\perp = V$ in any unitary space V.
5. Show in detail why any orthonormal set in a unitary space V can be extended to an orthonormal basis of V.
6. Show in detail why $U = U^{\perp\perp}$ for any subspace U of a unitary space V.
7. Prove Bessel's Inequality; $\|x\|^2 \ge \sum_i |(x, z_i)|^2$ for any orthonormal set $\{z_i\}$. (Hint: extend $\{z_i\}$ to an orthonormal basis of V.)
8. In the proof of Lemma 4, show why U is a subspace of V.
9. Find the norms of the scalar operators 0, 1, and c on any unitary space.
10. Let $\{z_1, \ldots, z_n\}$ be an orthonormal ordered basis of an n-dimensional unitary space V and let f be the mapping of V onto complex Euclidean n-space defined $f(\sum c_i z_i) = [c_1, \ldots, c_n]$. Show that f is a 1–1 mapping and $(f(x), f(y)) = (x, y)$, $f(ax + by) = af(x) + bf(y)$ for all $x, y \in V$ and all scalars a, b.
11. Let T be an operator on a unitary space V and let U be a subspace of V invariant under T. Prove that $U^\perp$ is invariant under T^*.
12. Use Problem 10 to show that a scalar product can be defined on any complex vector space.
13. Prove that if U and W are complementary subspaces of a unitary space V, then $U^\perp$ and $W^\perp$ are also complementary.
14. If $\{z_1, \ldots, z_m\}$ is an orthonormal set of vectors, prove that the z_i are linearly independent. (Hint: $(\sum_i c_i z_i, z_j) = c_j$.)
15. Prove $(x, ay + bz) = \bar{a}(x, y) + \bar{b}(x, z)$ for any $x, y, z \in V$ and scalars a, b.
16. Prove $|(x, y)|^2 \le (x, x)(y, y)$ for any $x, y \in V$.

Lecture 5–2

Types of Operators on Unitary Spaces. Let T be an operator on a unitary space V. We say that T is *self-adjoint* (or *Hermitian*) if $T = T^*$. We say that T is *normal* if $TT^* = T^*T$. Of course if T is self-adjoint it must also be normal. On the other hand there do exist normal operators that are not self-adjoint; consider, for example, the scalar operator c where c is not a real scalar. The operator T is said to be a *perpendicular projection* if $T^2 = T = T^*$; in other words a perpendicular projection is a self-adjoint projection. We say that T is a *partial isometry* if TT^* is a perpendicular projection. We say that a nonsingular operator T is *unitary* if $T^* = T^{-1}$. These definitions give rise to the following results.

Theorem 1. *The following are equivalent for an operator T on a unitary space V.*
(1) $T = 0$.
(2) $(xT, x) = 0$ *for all* $x \in V$.
(3) $(xT, y) = 0$ *for all* $x, y \in V$.

PROOF. The implication $(1) \Rightarrow (2)$ is evident. To obtain $(3) \Rightarrow (1)$ set $y = xT$ in (3) and observe that $(xT, xT) = 0$ and $xT = 0$ for all $x \in V$. It remains only to prove $(2) \Rightarrow (3)$. From (2) we have for all $x, y \in V$,

$$0 = ((x + y)T, x + y) = (xT, x) + (yT, y) + (xT, y) + (yT, x)$$
$$0 = ((x - y)T, x - y) = (xT, x) + (yT, y) - (xT, y) - (yT, x)$$

from which it follows that $(xT, y) + (yT, x) = 0$.

Furthermore,

$$0 = ((x + iy)T, x + iy) = (xT, x) + (yT, y) - i(xT, y) + i(yT, x)$$
$$0 = ((x - iy)T, x - iy) = (xT, x) + (yT, y) + i(xT, y) - i(yT, x)$$

from which it follows that $(xT, y) - (yT, x) = 0$. Finally

$$2(xT, y) = [(xT, y) + (yT, x)] + [(xT, y) - (yT, x)] = 0.$$

Theorem 2. *For an operator T on a unitary space V the following are equivalent.*
(1) T *is normal.*
(2) $(xT, yT) = (xT^*, yT^*)$ *for all* $x, y \in V$.
(3) $\|xT\| = \|xT^*\|$ *for all* $x \in V$.

136

PROOF. To prove $(1) \Rightarrow (2)$ assume that T is normal. Then for any $x, y \in V$, $(xT, yT) = (xTT^*, y) = (xT^*T, y) = (xT^*, yT^*)$.

To prove $(2) \Rightarrow (3)$ assume (2). Then for any $x \in V$ we have $\|xT\|^2 = (xT, xT) = (xT^*, xT^*) = \|xT^*\|^2$.

To prove $(3) \Rightarrow (1)$ assume (3). Then for any $x \in V$ we have

$$(xTT^*, x) = (xT, xT) = \|xT\|^2 = \|xT^*\|^2$$
$$= (xT^*, xT^*) = (xT^*T, x)$$

and $(x(TT^* - T^*T), x) = 0$. By Theorem 1, $TT^* - T^*T = 0$ and $T^*T = TT^*$.

Theorem 3. *An operator T on a unitary space V is self-adjoint iff (xT, x) is real for all $x \in V$.*

PROOF. Assume T is self-adjoint. For any $x \in V$ we have $(xT, x) = (x, xT^*) = (x, xT) = \overline{(xT, x)}$ and (xT, x) is real.

Now assume (xT, x) is real for all $x \in V$. Then $(xT, x) = \overline{(xT, x)} = (x, xT) = (xT^*, x)$ and $(x(T - T^*), x) = 0$. By Theorem 1, $T - T^* = 0$ and $T = T^*$. This completes the proof.

Theorem 4. *For all normal operators T, $\|T^2\| = \|T\|^2$.*

PROOF. We have

$$\|T^2\| \, \|T^{*2}\| \geq \|T^2 T^{*2}\| = \|(TT^*)^2\|$$

because T is normal. By Lecture 5-1, $\|(TT^*)^2\| = \|TT^*\| \, \|TT^*\| = \|T\|^2 \, \|T^*\|^2$. But $\|T^2\| \leq \|T\|^2$, and $\|T^{*2}\| \leq \|T^*\|^2$. It follows that

$$\|T^2\| \, \|T^{*2}\| \geq \|T\|^2 \, \|T^*\|^2 \geq \|T^2\| \, \|T^{*2}\|$$

and

$$\|T^2\| = \|T\|^2, \quad \|T^{*2}\| = \|T^*\|^2.$$

Theorem 5. *The following are equivalent for an operator T on a unitary space V.*

(1) T is unitary.
(2) $\|xT\| = \|x\|$ for all $x \in V$.
(3) $(xT, yT) = (x, y)$ for all $x, y \in V$.

PROOF. Assume (2). Then for any $x \in V$ we have $(x, x) = (xT, xT) = (xTT^*, x)$ and $(x(1 - TT^*), x) = 0$. By Theorem 1, $1 - TT^* = 0$ and $T^*T = 1$. Consequently $(2) \Rightarrow (1)$.

Assume (1). Then for any $x, y \in V$ we have $(xT, yT) = (xTT^*, y) = (x, y)$. Consequently $(1) \Rightarrow (3)$.

Now assume (3). By setting $y = x$ in (3) we have $\|xT\|^2 = (xT, xT) = (x, x) = \|x\|^2$. Consequently $(3) \Rightarrow (2)$.

Theorem 6. *For an operator P on a unitary space V the following are equivalent.*

(1) P is a perpendicular projection.
(2) $(xP, xP) = (x, xP)$ for all $x \in V$.
(3) $PP^* = P$.
(4) $P^*P = P$.

PROOF. If (1) holds then

$$(x(P - 1), xP) = (xP, xP) - (x, xP) = (x, xPP^*) - (x, xP)$$
$$= (x, xP^2) - (x, xP) = (x, xP) - (x, xP) = 0$$

for all $x \in V$, and hence (1) $\Rightarrow$ (2).

If (2) holds then

$$0 = (xP, xP) - (x, xP) = (x, xPP^*) - (x, xP) = (x, x(PP^* - P))$$

for all $x \in V$ and by Theorem 1, $PP^* - P = 0$. Thus (2) $\Rightarrow$ (3).

If (3) holds then $PP^* = P$, and by taking adjoints we see $PP^* = P^* = P$ and $P = P^2$. Thus (3) $\Rightarrow$ (1), and clearly (1), (2), and (3) are equivalent. In a similar way it follows that (4) $\Rightarrow$ (1) and (1) $\Rightarrow$ (4).

Lemma 1.   *Let T be an operator on a unitary space V and let N be the null space of T. Then $VT^* = N^\perp$ and N is the null space of TT^*.*

PROOF. Suppose $x \in N$ and $y \in V$. Then $0 = (xT, y) = (x, yT^*)$ and it follows that $VT^* \subset N^\perp$. On the other hand suppose $z \in N^\perp$ and $z \perp VT^*$; then $0 = (z, (zT)T^*) = (zT, zT)$ and $z \in N$, $z = 0$. Thus $VT^* = N^\perp$. Likewise VT is the orthogonal complement of the null space of T^*.

If $z \in N$, then $zTT^* = 0$. If $(zT)T^* = 0$, then $0 = (zTT^*, z) = (zT, zT)$, $zT = 0$ and $z \in N$. This completes the proof of Lemma 1.

Theorem 7.   *Let N be the null space of the operator T. Then T is a perpendicular projection iff $zT = z$ for each $z \in N^\perp$.*

PROOF. Assume that T is a perpendicular projection. Then $T = T^*$ and $VT = N^\perp$. Thus if $z \in N^\perp$, then $z = xT$ for some $x \in V$ and $zT = xT^2 = xT = z$.

Now assume $zT = z$ for every $z \in N^\perp$. If $x \in N$, $y \in N^\perp$ we have

$$((x + y)TT^*, x + y) = (xTT^* + yTT^*, x + y) = (yT^*, x + y)$$
$$= (yT^*, y) = (y, yT) = (y, y) = (y, x + y)$$
$$= (yT, x + y) = ((x + y)T, x + y).$$

Thus for any $z \in V$, $(z(TT^* - T), z) = 0$ and $TT^* - T = 0$. This concludes the proof.

If U is a subspace of the unitary space V note that there is only one perpendicular projection with null space U. Furthermore $U^\perp$ is its range.

Theorem 8.   *Let T be an operator on a unitary space V with null space N and let N_1 denote the null space of T^*. Then the following are equivalent.*
(1)   *T is a partial isometry.*
(2)   *T^* is a partial isometry.*
(3)   *$\|z\| = \|zT\|$ for all $z \in N^\perp$.*
(4)   *$\|z\| = \|zT^*\|$ for all $z \in N_1^\perp$.*

PROOF. Assume (1). Then TT^* is the perpendicular projection with null space N. By Theorem 7, if $z \in N^\perp$ then $\|z\|^2 = (z, z) = (zTT^*, z) = (zT, zT) = \|zT\|^2$ and clearly (1) $\Rightarrow$ (3).

Now assume (3). Then $VTT^* \subset VT^* = N^\perp$ and $N^\perp$ is invariant under TT^*. If $z \in N^\perp$, then $(z, z) = \|z\|^2 = \|zT\|^2 = (zT, zT) = (zTT^*, z)$ and by Theorem 1, the contraction of TT^* to $N^\perp$ is the identity mapping on $N^\perp$. On the other hand N is the null space of TT^* and by Theorem 7, TT^* is a perpendicular projection. Consequently we have (1) $\Leftrightarrow$ (3).

In a like manner (2) $\Leftrightarrow$ (4). It remains only to prove (1) $\Rightarrow$ (2) (the converse is proved if T is replaced by T^*). Assume (1). Then TT^* is the perpendicular projection with null space N, and consequently $T = (TT^*)T$. (Problem 1.) Hence $(T^*T)(T^*T)^* = T^*(TT^*)T = T^*T$ and T^*T is also a perpendicular projection by Theorem 6. Thus T^* is a partial isometry and the proof is complete.

Note that a unitary operator is a partial isometry. However the converse statement is not true; consider for example a perpendicular projection on V with nonzero null space. A perpendicular projection is a partial isometry. However the converse statement is not true; for example let V be a 2-dimensional unitary space with orthonormal basis $\{z_1, z_2\}$ and let T be the operator for which $z_1 T = z_2, z_2 T = 0$. We have

Theorem 9. *Let P be a projection on a unitary space V. Then P is a perpendicular projection iff $\|zP\| \leq \|z\|$ for all $z \in V$.*

PROOF. Let N denote the null space of P. Assume first that P is a perpendicular projection. Then if $x \in N, y \in N^\perp$ we have

$$((x + y)P, (x + y)P) = (yP, yP) = (y, y)$$
$$\leq (x, x) + (y, y) = (x + y, x + y),$$

and clearly $\|zP\| \leq \|z\|$ for all $z \in V$.

Now assume that $\|zP\| \leq \|z\|$ for all $z \in V$. For $z \in N^\perp$ set $y = zP - z$, and observe that $yP = (zP - z)P = zP^2 - zP = zP - zP = 0$ and $y \in N$. Thus $(z, y) = 0$ and

$$(z, z) \geq (zP, zP) = (y + z, y + z) = (y, y) + (z, z)$$

and $(y, y) = 0$. It follows that $y = 0$ and $zP = z$. By Theorem 7, P is a perpendicular projection.

Theorem 10. *Let T be an operator on a unitary space V. Then*
(1) $|(zT, z)| \leq \|T\| (z, z)$ *for all $z \in V$,*
(2) *if T is self-adjoint and if M is a number such that $|(zT, z)| \leq M(z, z)$ for all $z \in V$, then $\|T\| \leq M$.*

PROOF. To prove (1) we have $|(zT, z)| \leq \|zT\| \|z\| \leq \|T\| \|z\| \|z\| = \|T\| (z, z)$ for all $z \in V$.

To prove (2) let $z \in V$ with $zT \neq 0$ and $\|z\| = 1$, and put $y = \|zT\|^{-1}(zT)$. Then $(zT, y) = (zT, \|zT\|^{-1}(zT)) = \|zT\| = (z, yT) = (yT, z)$ and

$$4M = M(2\|z\|^2 + 2\|y\|^2) = M(\|z + y\|^2 + \|z - y\|^2)$$
$$\geq ((z + y)T, z + y) - ((z - y)T, z - y)$$
$$= 2[(yT, z) + (zT, y)] = 4\|zT\|.$$

Hence $M \geq \|zT\|$ and it follows that $\|T\| \leq M$.

On the other hand (2) does not remain valid if we drop the assumption that T is self-adjoint. For example let V be a 2-dimensional unitary space and let T have the matrix $\begin{bmatrix} 0 & 1 \\ 0 & 0 \end{bmatrix}$ relative to the orthonormal basis $\{v, w\}$. Then

$$|((av + bw)T, av + bw)| = |(aw, av + bw)|$$
$$= |a\bar{b}| \leq \tfrac{1}{2}(|a|^2 + |b|^2)$$
$$= \tfrac{1}{2}(av + bw, av + bw).$$

However $\|T\| = 1$ and $1 > \tfrac{1}{2}$.

Theorem 11. *Let T be an operator on a unitary space V and let c be an eigenvalue of T. Then*

(1) $|c| \leq \|T\|$,
(2) $\bar{c}$ *is an eigenvalue of* T^*,
(3) $p(c)$ *is an eigenvalue of* $p(T)$ *for every polynomial* p,
(4) *if T is self-adjoint, then c is real,*
(5) *if T is unitary, then $|c| = 1$,*
(6) *if T is a projection, then $c = 0$ or $c = 1$.*

PROOF.   To prove (1) let z be an eigenvector for the eigenvalue c. Then $\|zT\| = \|cz\| = |c| \|z\|$ and it follows that $\|T\| \geq |c|$. To prove (2) observe that if $T - c$ is singular, $(T - c)^* = T^* - \bar{c}$ is also singular. To prove (3) observe that there exists a polynomial q such that $p(T) - p(c) = (T - c)q(T)$. (Problem 2.) Thus if $T - c$ is singular so is $p(T) - p(c)$.

To prove (4), let T be self-adjoint and let z be an eigenvector for the eigenvalue c. Then $(zT, z) = (cz, z) = c(z, z) = (z, zT) = (z, cz) = \bar{c}(z, z)$ and $c = \bar{c}$.

To prove (5) let T be unitary and let z be an eigenvector for the eigenvalue c. Then $(z, z) = (zT, zT) = (cz, cz) = |c|^2(z, z)$ and $|c|^2 = 1$.

To prove (6), let T be a projection and let z be an eigenvector for the eigenvalue c. Set $z = ax + by$ where $x \in VT$, $y \in V(1 - T)$. Recall that VT and $V(1 - T)$ are complementary subspaces of V. Then $(ax + by)T = cax + cby = ax$. It follows that $(ca - a)x = 0$ and $cby = 0$. If $c \neq 0$, then $by = 0$, $ax \neq 0$, $(c - 1)(ax) = 0$ and $c - 1 = 0$.

Theorem 12. *For two perpendicular projections P and Q on a unitary space V the following are equivalent.*

(1) $PQ = QP = P$.
(2) $\|zP\| \leq \|zQ\|$ *for all* $z \in V$.
(3) $VP \subset VQ$.
(4) $PQ = P$.
(5) $QP = P$.
(6) $(zP, z) \leq (zQ, z)$ *for all* $z \in V$.

PROOF.   We shall prove the implications $(1) \Rightarrow (3) \Rightarrow (4) \Rightarrow$ $(5) \Rightarrow (1) \Rightarrow (2) \Leftrightarrow (6) \Rightarrow (2) \Rightarrow (3)$.

$(1) \Rightarrow (3)$. If $PQ = QP = P$ then $VP = (VP)Q \subset VQ$.

$(3) \Rightarrow (4)$. If $VP \subset VQ$, then for $z \in V$ we have $zP \in VQ$ and $(zP)Q = zP$.

$(4) \Rightarrow (5)$. If $PQ = P$, then $P = P^* = (PQ)^* = QP$.

$(5) \Rightarrow (1)$. If $QP = P$, then $P = P^* = (QP)^* = PQ = QP$.

$(1) \Rightarrow (2)$. If $PQ = QP = P$, then $\|zP\| = \|(zQ)P\| \leq \|zQ\|$.

$(2) \Leftrightarrow (6)$. We have $(zP, zP) = (zP^2, z) = (zP, z)$ and $(zQ, zQ) = (zQ^2, z) = (zQ, z)$.

$(2) \Rightarrow (3)$. If $\|zP\| \leq \|zQ\|$, then for $z \perp VQ$ we have $zQ = 0$, $zP = 0$ and $z \perp VP$. Thus $(VQ)^{\perp} \subset (VP)^{\perp}$ and $VP \subset VQ$.

Theorem 13. *For two perpendicular projections P and Q on a unitary space V the following are equivalent.*

(1) $PQ = 0$.
(2) $VP \perp VQ$.
(3) $P \perp Q$.

PROOF.   If $PQ = 0$ then $V(PQ) = (VP)Q = (0)$ and $VP \perp VQ$. Thus $(1) \Rightarrow (2)$. If $VP \perp VQ$ then $(VP)Q = (0) = (VQ)P$ and $PQ = QP = 0$. Hence $(2) \Rightarrow (3)$. Finally, $(3) \Rightarrow (1)$ is clear.

Problems for Lecture 5—2

1.   In the proof of $(1) \Rightarrow (3)$ in Theorem 8 explain why $T = (TT^*)T$.

2.   In the proof of (3) in Theorem 11 explain why there exists a polynomial q such that $p(T) - p(c) = (T - c)q(T)$.

3.   Let P and Q be perpendicular projections on a unitary space V. Prove that $P \leq Q$ iff $VP \subset VQ$. Prove that $P \leq Q$ iff the null space of Q is a subspace of the null space of P.

4.   Let A be the matrix of an operator T relative to an ordered orthonormal basis.

  (a)   Prove that the matrix of T^* relative to the same basis is found by replacing each entry in the transpose of A with its conjugate.

(b)   If T is self-adjoint, prove that det T is real.

(c)   If T is a unitary operator, prove that $|\det T| = 1$.

5.   Prove that a normal operator has the same range and null space as its adjoint.

6.   Let $\{z_1, \ldots, z_n\}$ and $\{w_1, \ldots, w_n\}$ be ordered orthonormal bases of a unitary space V and let T be the operator on V for which $w_i = z_i T$ for each $i = 1, \ldots, n$. Prove that T is a unitary operator.

7.   Let T be a nonsingular operator on a unitary space V. Prove that T^* is also nonsingular and $T^{*-1} = (T^{-1})^*$.

$\mathcal{L}$ecture 5–3

The Spectral Theorem and the Polar Decomposition of an Operator. In this lecture we will show that any normal operator is a linear combination of pairwise orthogonal perpendicular projections. The first result is known as the *Spectral Theorem* for normal operators.

Theorem 1. *Let T be an operator on a unitary space V, let its distinct eigenvalues be $c_1, \ldots, c_k$ and let P_i be the perpendicular projection whose range is the subspace V_{c_i} as defined in Lecture 4-4. Then the following are equivalent.*

(1) *T is normal.*
(2) *$\|zT^*\| \leq \|zT\|$ for all $z \in V$.*
(3) *The P_i are pairwise orthogonal and $T = \sum_i c_i P_i$, $1 = \sum_i P_i$.*
(4) *$\|zT\| \leq \|zT^*\|$ for all $z \in V$.*

Furthermore if T is normal and if $d_1, \ldots, d_k$ are any scalars, then there exists a polynomial p such that $p(T) = \sum_i d_i P_i$.

PROOF. We shall first prove $(3) \Rightarrow (1) \Rightarrow (2) \Rightarrow (3)$ and then $(4) \Leftrightarrow (1)$.

$(3) \Rightarrow (1)$. Since $T = \sum_i c_i P_i$ we have $T^* = (\sum_i c_i P_i)^* = \sum_i \bar{c}_i P_i$ and

$$TT^* = (\sum c_i P_i)(\sum \bar{c}_j P_j) = \sum_{ij} c_i \bar{c}_j P_i P_j$$
$$= \sum_{ij} c_i \bar{c}_j P_j P_i \qquad = (\sum_j \bar{c}_j P_j)(\sum_i c_i P_i) = T^*T$$

because the P_i commute.

$(1) \Rightarrow (2)$. If T is normal we have $(zT, zT) = (z, zTT^*) = (z, zT^*T) = (zT^*, zT^*)$.

$(2) \Rightarrow (3)$. Select $z \in V_{c_i}$ such that $z(T - c_i)^2 = 0$ and set

$$w = z(T - c_i), y = wT^* - \bar{c}_i w.$$

Then

$$(w, wT^*) = (wT, w) = (c_i w, w) = c_i(w, w),$$
$$(w, y) = (w, wT^* - \bar{c}_i w) = c_i(w, w) - c_i(w, w) = 0,$$
$$|c_i|^2(w, w) = (wT, wT) \geq (wT^*, wT^*)$$
$$= (\bar{c}_i w + y, \bar{c}_i w + y) = |c_i|^2(w, w) + (y, y)$$

and $y = 0$. Thus

$$wT^* = \bar{c}_i w, \quad (w, w) = (z(T - c_i), w) = (z, w(T^* - \bar{c}_i)) = 0$$

and $w = 0$. We have shown that if $z(T - c_i)^2 = 0$,

then $z(T - c_i) = 0$. It follows that V_{c_i} is the null space of $T - c_i$ (Problem 2).

We claim that $V_{c_i} \perp V_{c_j}$ if $i \neq j$. Let $w \in V_{c_i}$, $z \in V_{c_j}$, and recall that we have just proved that $wT^* = \bar{c}_i w$. Then $c_i(z, w) = (z, \bar{c}_i w) = (z, wT^*) = (zT, w) = (c_j z, w) = c_j(z, w)$ and $(c_i - c_j)(z, w) = 0$. Since $c_i \neq c_j$ we have $(z, w) = 0$.

Now $V_{c_j} P_i = (0)$ if $i \neq j$, and it follows that $\sum_{j \neq i} \oplus V_{c_j}$ is the null space of P_i. Thus the P_i are pairwise orthogonal perpendicular projections and $\sum_i P_i = 1$. Also T coincides with $\sum_i c_i P_i$ on each V_{c_i} and therefore coincides with $\sum_i c_i P_i$ on V.

$(4) \Leftrightarrow (1)$. It follows from $(1) \Leftrightarrow (2)$ that (4) is equivalent to the assertion that T^* is normal, i.e., T is normal.

Finally assume that T is normal and $d_1, \ldots, d_k$ are any scalars. We have $T = \sum c_i P_i$, $T^2 = (\sum_i c_i P_i)(\sum_j c_j P_j) = \sum_i c_i^2 P_i$, and by induction on n, $T^n = \sum_i c_i^n P_i$. For any polynomial q we clearly have $q(T) = \sum_i q(c_i) P_i$. Let p be a polynomial for which $p(c_j) = d_j$ for all i; for example, $p(x) = \sum_i d_i [\prod_{j \neq i} (c_i - c_j)^{-1}(x - c_j)]$. Then $p(T) = \sum_i d_i P_i$ and the proof is complete.

Observe also that if T is normal, then T^* is a polynomial in T. Conversely if T^* is a polynomial in T, then T must be normal. For T normal, an operator S commutes with T iff S commutes with each P_i; this follows because each P_i is a polynomial in T, and T is a linear combination of the P_i. A normal operator can be expressed in only one way as a linear combination of pairwise orthogonal projections with distinct coefficients (except for the order of the terms). For if $\sum_i a_i Q_i$ is such a linear combination with $\sum_i Q_i = 1$, then the a_i are the distinct eigenvalues of $\sum_i a_i Q_i$ and Q_j is the perpendicular projection on the null space of the operator $\sum_i a_i Q_i - a_j$ for each j (Problem 3). We call the linear combination in (3) the *Spectral Form* of T.

We say that an operator T is *nonnegative* if $(zT, z) \geq 0$ for all $z \in V$. It follows from Theorem 3 of Lecture 5-2 that a nonnegative operator is normal. It is easy to see from the Spectral Form that a normal operator is nonnegative iff its eigenvalues are nonnegative (Problem 4). Suppose T is a nonnegative operator and $(\sum c_i^{\frac{1}{2}} P_i)^2 = \sum c_i P_i = T$. We claim that if S is a nonnegative operator such that $S^2 = T$, then $S = \sum c_i^{\frac{1}{2}} P_i$. To see this let $\sum_j a_j Q_j$ be the Spectral Form of S. Then $S^2 = \sum_j a_j^2 Q_j = \sum_i c_i P_i$ and the operators $a_j^2 Q_j$ are the operators $c_i P_i$ in some order by the uniqueness of the Spectral Form of T. Hence $S = \sum_i c_i^{\frac{1}{2}} P_i$. This operator S is often denoted $T^{\frac{1}{2}}$.

The following result defines the *polar decomposition* of an operator.

Theorem 2. *Let T be an operator on a unitary space V with null space N. Then there are a unique nonnegative operator W and a unique partial isometry U, each with null space N, such that $T = WU$. Furthermore T is normal iff $WU = UW$. If T is normal, then U is also normal.*

PROOF. For any $z \in V$ we have $(zTT^*, z) = (zT, zT) \geq 0$ and TT^* is nonnegative. Furthermore

$$\|z(TT^*)^{\frac{1}{2}}\|^2 = (z(TT^*)^{\frac{1}{2}}, z(TT^*)^{\frac{1}{2}}) = (zTT^*, z) = \|zT\|^2$$

and the null space of $(TT^*)^{\frac{1}{2}}$ is N. Since $(TT^*)^{\frac{1}{2}}$ is normal we have $V(TT^*)^{\frac{1}{2}} = N^\perp$, and any vector $z \in N^\perp$ can be uniquely expressed $z = w(TT^*)^{\frac{1}{2}}$ for some $w \in N^\perp$. We define the operator U as follows; for $z \in N$, set $zU = 0$ and for $z = w(TT^*)^{\frac{1}{2}}$, $w \in N^\perp$, set $zU = wT$. The verification that U so defined is actually an operator on V is left to the reader (Problem 5).

If $z \in N^\perp$ and $z = w(TT^*)^{\frac{1}{2}}$, $w \in N^\perp$, we have $(zU, zU) = (wT, wT) = (w(TT^*)^{\frac{1}{2}}, w(TT^*)^{\frac{1}{2}}) = (z, z)$. Plainly the null space of U is N and by Theorem 8 of Lecture 5-2, U is a partial isometry. Furthermore T and $(TT^*)^{\frac{1}{2}}U$ coincide on N and $N^\perp$, and consequently $T = (TT^*)^{\frac{1}{2}}U$. This proves existence.

To prove uniqueness, suppose W_0 is a nonnegative operator and U_0 is a partial isometry satisfying $T = W_0 U_0$ and the null spaces of U_0 and W_0 are both N. Then $U_0 U_0^*$ is the perpendicular projection with range $N^\perp$ and $(W_0 U_0)(W_0 U_0)^* = W_0(U_0 U_0^*)W_0 = W_0^2 = TT^*$. It follows that $W_0 = (TT^*)^{\frac{1}{2}}$. And $0 = T - T = (TT^*)^{\frac{1}{2}}(U - U_0)$ and U coincides with U_0 on $V(TT^*)^{\frac{1}{2}} = N^\perp$. But N is the null space of U and of U_0 so $U = U_0$.

Finally we have $T^*T = [(TT^*)^{\frac{1}{2}}U]^*[(TT^*)^{\frac{1}{2}}U] = U^*TT^*U$. If T is normal then $VT = N^\perp = V(U^*U)$ and both U^*U and UU^* are the perpendicular projection with range $N^\perp$. Hence $U(TT^*) = U(T^*T) = (UU^*)(TT^*)U = TT^*U$ and therefore U commutes with $(TT^*)^{\frac{1}{2}}$ because $(TT^*)^{\frac{1}{2}}$ equals a polynomial in TT^*. On the other hand if U commutes with $(TT^*)^{\frac{1}{2}}$, then $VU \subset V(TT^*)^{\frac{1}{2}} = N^\perp$ (Problem 7) and since dim $N^\perp = $ dim VU we have $VU = N^\perp$. Hence U^*U is the perpendicular projection with range $N^\perp$ and $T^*T = U^*U(TT^*) = TT^*$ and the proof is complete.

From the Spectral Theorem we can draw the following conclusions about normal operators.

Theorem 3. *Let T be a normal operator. Then*

(1)   *T is self-adjoint iff each eigenvalue of T is real.*
(2)   *T is a perpendicular projection iff each eigenvalue of T is either 0 or 1.*
(3)   *T is unitary iff each eigenvalue of T has absolute value 1.*
(4)   *T is a partial isometry iff each nonzero eigenvalue of T has absolute value 1.*

PROOF. Throughout the argument let $\sum c_i P_i$ be the Spectral Form of T.

(1) $T = \sum c_i P_i$ and $T^* = \sum \bar{c}_i P_i$. Hence $T = T^*$ iff $c_i = \bar{c}_i$ for all i.
(2) $TT^* = (\sum c_i P_i)(\sum \bar{c}_j P_j) = \sum c_i \bar{c}_i P_i$. Hence $TT^* = T$ iff $c_i = c_i \bar{c}_i$ for all i.

(3) $TT^* = \sum c_i \bar{c}_i P_i = 1$ iff $c_i \bar{c}_i = 1$ for all i.
(4) $TT^* = \sum c_i \bar{c}_i P_i$ is a projection iff $|c_i|^2 = 0$ or 1 for each i.

We conclude with more necessary and sufficient conditions that T be normal.

Theorem 4.   *For an operator T on a unitary space V the following are equivalent.*

(1)   *T is normal,*
(2)   *if U is a subspace invariant under T, then U is invariant under T^*,*
(3)   *if U is a subspace invariant under T, then $U^\perp$ is invariant under T,*
(4)   *if U is a subspace invariant under T^*, then U is invariant under T,*
(5)   *if U is a subspace invariant under T^*, then $U^\perp$ is invariant under T^*.*

PROOF.   We will prove $(1) \Rightarrow (2) \Rightarrow (3) \Rightarrow (1)$ and $(4) \Leftrightarrow (5) \Leftrightarrow (1)$.

$(1) \Rightarrow (2)$. If T is normal and if U is invariant under T, then T^* equals a polynomial in T and U is also invariant under T^*.

$(2) \Rightarrow (3)$. Suppose U is invariant under T^* and select $z \in U$, $v \in U^\perp$. Then $0 = (zT^*, v) = (z, vT)$, $vT \in U^\perp$ and $U^\perp T \subset U^\perp$.

$(3) \Rightarrow (1)$. Assume (3) and let u_1 be an eigenvector of T for the eigenvalue c_1. Let U_1 be the 1-dimensional subspace spanned by u_1. Then $U_1^\perp$ is invariant under T and there is an eigenvector $u_2 \in U_1^\perp$ for the eigenvalue c_2, say (use the contraction of T to $U_1^\perp$). Let U_2 be the subspace spanned by u_2. Then $(U_1 \oplus U_2)^\perp$ is invariant under T and there exists an eigenvector $u_3 \in (U_1 \oplus U_2)^\perp$ of T for the eigenvalue c_3, and so on. Finally we can express V as the direct sum of 1-dimensional pairwise orthogonal subspaces $U_1, \ldots, U_n$ such that $T - c_i$ annihilates U_i for each index i. (The scalars c_i need not be distinct.) Let P_i be the perpendicular projection with range U_i. Then T coincides with $\sum_i c_i P_i$ on each U_i, and hence $T = \sum_i c_i P_i$ on V. But then $T^* = \sum_i \bar{c}_i P_i$ and

$$T^*T = \left(\sum_j \bar{c}_j P_j\right)\left(\sum_i c_i P_i\right) = \sum_i |c_i|^2 P_i$$
$$= \left(\sum_j c_j P_j\right)\left(\sum_i \bar{c}_i P_i\right) = TT^*.$$

This proves $(1) \Rightarrow (2) \Rightarrow (3) \Rightarrow (1)$. Replacing T with T^* we see that (4) and (5) are each equivalent to the assertion that T^* is normal. But T^* is normal iff T is normal. This concludes the proof.

Problems for Lecture 5—3

1.   In the proof of Theorem 1 explain why for any polynomial q we have $q(T) = \sum_i q(c_i) P_i$ where $T = \sum_i c_i P_i$ and the P_i are pairwise orthogonal projections.

2. In the proof of (2) $\Rightarrow$ (3) in Theorem 1 explain why V_{c_i} is the null space of $T - c_i$.

3. In the paragraph following the proof of Theorem 1 explain why Q_j is the perpendicular projection on the null space of $\sum_i a_i Q_i - a_j$.

4. Prove that a normal operator is nonnegative iff all its eigenvalues are nonnegative.

5. In the proof of Theorem 2 show that U, as defined, is actually an operator on V.

6. If T is nonnegative on a unitary space V, prove that T and $T^{\frac{1}{2}}$ have the same range and null space.

7. In the last paragraph of the proof of Theorem 2 explain why $VU \subset V(TT^*)^{\frac{1}{2}}$.

8. If T is an operator with null space N on a unitary space V, and if P is the perpendicular projection with range $N^{\perp}$, prove that $T = PT$.

9. If S and T are nonnegative operators on a unitary space and $S + T = 0$, prove $S = T = 0$.

10. Prove that if T is normal, then T^* equals a polynomial in T.

11. Let T be a Hermitian operator on a unitary space V. Prove that $(TT^*)^{\frac{1}{2}} + T$ and $(T^*T)^{\frac{1}{2}} - T$ are both nonnegative and $[(TT^*)^{\frac{1}{2}} + T][(T^*T)^{\frac{1}{2}} - T] = 0$. If S_1 and S_2 are nonnegative operators such that $S_1 S_2 = 0$, $T = S_1 - S_2$ prove that $S_1 = \frac{1}{2}[(TT^*)^{\frac{1}{2}} + T]$, $S_2 = \frac{1}{2}[(TT^*)^{\frac{1}{2}} - T]$.

12. If T is nonnegative, prove that $\det T \geq 0$.

13. Let S and T be similar normal operators on a unitary space V. Prove that there exists a unitary operator U such that $UTU^{-1} = S$. (Hint: compare the spectral forms of S and T and use Problem 6 of Lecture 5-2.)

14. Let A be an n by n matrix satisfying $\bar{A}^t A = A\bar{A}^t$ where $\bar{A}^t$ denotes the result of conjugating each entry in the transpose of A. Prove that there exists an n by n matrix B satisfying $\bar{B}^t B = I_n$ such that $BA\bar{B}^t$ is diagonal. (Hint: use the Spectral Theorem and Problem 4 of Lecture 5-2.)

15. Let A be an n by n complex matrix. Prove that $\bar{A}^t A = I_n$ iff the rows (or columns) of A form an orthonormal basis of complex Euclidean n-space.

16. Let A be a real n by n matrix such that $A^t = A$. Prove that there exists a real matrix B satisfying $B^t B = I_n$ such that BAB^t is diagonal. (Hint: show that all the eigenvalues of A are real and use a complexification argument.)

17. Show by example that in Problem 16 we cannot replace $A^t = A$ with $A^t A = AA^t$.

18. Prove that 2 normal operators on a unitary space are similar if they have the same characteristic polynomial.

$\mathcal{L}$ecture 5-4

Self-Adjoint Operator Algebras. Throughout this lecture M will be an operator algebra on a unitary space V with null space (0). We say that M is *self-adjoint* if $T \in M$ implies $T^* \in M$; i.e., $M^* \subset M$. Taking adjoints we see that $M = M^{**} \subset M^*$ and $M = M^*$. Note that if M is self-adjoint then M' is also self-adjoint; if $T \in M'$ and M is self-adjoint then $S^*T = TS^*$ for all $S \in M$ and thus $(S^*T)^* = (TS^*)^*$; i.e., $T^*S = ST^*$ and $T^* \in M'$.

We say that M is *orthogonally completely reducible* if for every subspace U invariant under M, $U^\perp$ is also invariant under M. Note that if M is orthogonally completely reducible, then M is completely reducible (Part 4). It is interesting that the self-adjoint operator algebras are precisely the orthogonally completely reducible operator algebras as we now prove.

Theorem 1. *Let M be an operator algebra on the unitary space V with null space (0). Then the following are equivalent.*
(1) *M is self-adjoint.*
(2) *M is orthogonally completely reducible.*

PROOF. $(1) \Rightarrow (2)$. Suppose M is self-adjoint and U is a subspace invariant under M. Then for any $T \in M$, we have $T^* \in M$, $UT^* \subset U$ and $U^\perp T \subset U^\perp$. Hence $U^\perp M \subset U^\perp$.

$(2) \Rightarrow (1)$. Now assume that M is orthogonally completely reducible. The nomenclature in the remainder of the proof will be that of Lecture 4-7. Since V is finite-dimensional there exists an M-irreducible subspace U_1 of V. Then $U_1^\perp$ is M-invariant and there exists an M-irreducible subspace U_2 of $U_1^\perp$ if $U_1 \neq V$. Continuing in this way we can find M-irreducible subspaces $U_1, \ldots, U_n$ such that $V = U_1 \oplus \cdots \oplus U_n$ and $U_i \subset (U_1 \oplus \cdots \oplus U_{i-1})^\perp$ for all i. Let P_i be the perpendicular projection with range U_i. Then $1 = \sum_i P_i$ and the P_i are pairwise orthogonal since the U_i are pairwise orthogonal. Furthermore $P_i \in M'$ for all i.

It suffices to show that M' is self-adjoint; for if M' is self-adjoint so also is M'', and $M = M''$ by Theorem 1 of Lecture 4-2.

If $T \in M'$ then $T = (\sum_i P_i) T (\sum_j P_j) = \sum_{ij} P_i T P_j$ and clearly T is the sum of operators $S \in M'$ satisfying $P_i S P_j = S$ for some indices i and j. If $S \in M'$ is such an operator, then by the proof of Theorem 2 of Lecture 4-7 there is an operator $S_1 \in M'$ such that

148

$P_j S_1 P_i = S_1$ and $SS_1 = P_i$, $S_1 S = P_j$. It suffices to show that every such operator S is a scalar multiple of some partial isometry R; for then $R*$ is a scalar multiple of S_1 (Problem 1) and clearly M' is self-adjoint. There are two possibilities: either $i = j$ or $i \neq j$.

For $i = j$, the contraction of $P_i M' P_i$ to $U_i = VP_i$ is the commutant of the contraction of $P_i M$ to U_i (see the proof of Lemma 4 of Lecture 4-7). But since U_i is M-irreducible, the contraction of $P_i M$ to U_i consists of all the operators on U_i by Theorem 2 of Lecture 4-7 and it follows that $P_i M' P_i$ consists of only the scalar multiples of P_i. Hence S is a scalar multiple of P_i and the proof is complete for the case $i = j$.

For $i \neq j$, the contraction of $(P_i + P_j) M' (P_i + P_j)$ to $U_i \oplus U_j = V(P_i + P_j)$ is the commutant of the contraction of $(P_i + P_j) M$ to $U_i \oplus U_j$. The set of all vectors of the form $z + zS$, $z \in U_i$, forms a subspace W of $U_i \oplus U_j$ (Problem 3). Furthermore W is M-invariant; for if $T \in M$, $z \in U_i$, then $(z + zS) T = zT + zST = zT + (zT)S$ and $zT \in U_i$. It is plain that dim $W = $ dim $U_i <$ dim $(U_i \oplus U_j)$. Let $v_1 + v_2$ be a nonzero vector in $(U_i \oplus U_j) \cap W^\perp$ where $v_1 \in U_i$ and $v_2 \in U_j$. It follows that $[(v_1 + v_2)M] \subset W^\perp$. Plainly $v_2 \neq 0$; if $v_2 = 0$, then $(v_1 + v_1 S, v_1 + v_2) = (v_1, v_1) > 0$ which is impossible. Similarly $v_1 \neq 0$; for if $v_1 = 0$, then

$$(v_2 S_1 + (v_2 S_1)S, v_1 + v_2) = (v_2, v_2) > 0.$$

Set $v = v_2 S_1$; then $vS = v_2$ and $v \neq 0$. We claim that v is a scalar multiple of v_1. If v is not a scalar multiple of v_1 then there is a $T \in M$ such that $v_1 T \neq 0$, $vT = 0$ (because the contraction of $P_i M$ to U_i consists of all the operators on U_i) and

$$
\begin{aligned}
0 &= (v_1 T + (v_1 T)S, (v_1 + v_2) T) \\
&= (v_1 T + (v_1 T)S, v_1 T + (vS) T) \\
&= (v_1 T + (v_1 T)S, v_1 T + (vT)S) \\
&= (v_1 T, v_1 T) > 0
\end{aligned}
$$

which is impossible. We can suppose that $v = -av_1$ for an appropriate nonzero scalar a.

So $v_1 + v_2 = v_1 + vS = v_1 - av_1 S$. Now let z be any vector in U_i and select $T \in M$ such that $v_1 T = z$. Then

$$
\begin{aligned}
0 &= ((v_1 - av_1 S) T, v_1 T + (v_1 T)S) \\
&= (v_1 T - a(v_1 T)S, v_1 T + (v_1 T)S) \\
&= (v_1 T, v_1 T) - a(v_1 TS, v_1 TS).
\end{aligned}
$$

For any $z \in U_i$ we have $(z, z) = a(zS, zS)$. Note that a is positive and set $R = a^{\frac{1}{2}} S$. Then $(zR, zR) = a(zS, zS) = (z, z)$. The null space of both the operators R and S is $U_i^\perp$ and $\|z\| = \|zR\|$ for all $z \in U_i$. By Theorem 8 of Lecture 5-2 R is a partial isometry. This completes the proof.

Next we find a relation between normal operators and commutative self adjoint operator algebras.

Theorem 2.   *Let M be a self-adjoint operator algebra on a unitary space V. Then the following are equivalent.*

(1)   *M is commutative.*

(2)   *every operator in M is normal.*

PROOF.   If M is commutative, then for every $T \in M$ we have $T^* \in M$ and $TT^* = T^*T$. Now assume every operator in M is normal. For S, $T \in M$ we have

$$SS^* + ST + T^*S^* + T^*T = (S + T^*)(S^* + T)$$

$$= (S + T^*)(S + T^*)^* = (S + T^*)^*(S + T^*)$$

$$= (S^* + T)(S + T^*) = S^*S + S^*T^* + TS + TT^*,$$

$$SS^* - iST + iT^*S^* + T^*T = (S + iT^*)(S^* - iT)$$

$$= (S + iT^*)(S + iT^*)^* = (S + iT^*)^*(S + iT^*)$$

$$= (S^* - iT)(S + iT^*) = S^*S + iS^*T^* - iTS + TT^*,$$

and it follows that $ST + T^*S^* = S^*T^* + TS$, $-iST + iT^*S^* = iS^*T^* - iTS$ and $-ST + T^*S^* = S^*T^* - TS$. From these equations it follows that $ST = TS$ and $S^*T^* = T^*S^*$. Hence M is commutative.

Theorem 3.   *Let M be a commutative self-adjoint operator algebra on a unitary space V. Then there exist pairwise orthogonal perpendicular projections $P_i \in M$ such that $1 = \sum_i P_i$ and every operator in M is a linear combination of the P_i. Furthermore $M = M'$ iff the range of each P_i has dimension 1.*

PROOF.   Since M is self-adjoint we see that M is the commutant of M', which is also self-adjoint and orthogonally completely reducible. By the proof of Theorem 1 there exist pairwise orthogonal perpendicular projections $P_i \in M$ such that $1 = \sum_i P_i$, and given any $T \in M$, $P_i TP_i = P_i^2 T = P_i T$ is a scalar multiple of P_i for each i. Then for any $T \in M$ we have $T = \sum_i P_i T$ and T is a linear combination of the projections P_i. Note that $M \subset M'$ since M is commutative.

If the range of each P_i has dimension 1, then $P_i TP_i$ is a scalar multiple of P_i for any operator T; in particular, for $T \in M'$ we have

$$T = \sum_{ij} P_i TP_j = \sum_{ij} TP_i P_j = \sum_i TP_i = \sum_i TP_i^2 = \sum_i P_i TP_i$$

and $M' \subset M$, $M' = M$.

On the other hand if the range of some P_i has dimension >1, then for any nonzero perpendicular projection Q satisfying $Q \leq P_i$, $Q \neq P_i$, we have $Q \in M' - M$ (Problem 6). This completes the proof.

The next result provides a partial converse to the statement that any self-adjoint operator algebra is completely reducible.

Theorem 4. *Let M be a completely reducible operator algebra on a complex vector space V. Then a scalar product can be defined on V so that M is self-adjoint on the resulting unitary space.*

PROOF. We know $M = M''$ and by the proof of Theorem 2 of Lecture 4-7 we have projections $P_1, \ldots, P_n \in M$ such that $\sum_i P_i = 1$ and VP_i is M'-irreducible for each i. We say that the projection P_i is equivalent to P_j if there exists a nonzero $T \in M$ such that $T = P_i T P_j$. Every projection P_i is equivalent to itself; for $P_i P_i P_i = P_i \neq 0$. If $S \in M$, $S \neq 0$ and $P_i S P_j = S$ it follows from the proof of Theorem 2 of Lecture 4-7 that there exists an operator $S_1 \in M$ satisfying $S_1 \neq 0$, $P_j S_1 P_i = S_1$. Thus if P_i is equivalent to P_j, P_j is equivalent to P_i. If furthermore there exists an $S_2 \in M$ satisfying $S_2 \neq 0$, and $P_j S_2 P_k = S_2$, then

$$P_i(SS_2)P_k = P_i(P_i S P_j)(P_j S_2 P_k)P_k$$
$$= (P_i S P_j)(P_j S_2 P_k) = SS_2$$

and

$$(S_1 S)S_2 = P_j S_2 = P_j(P_j S_2 P_k) = S_2 \neq 0, \ SS_2 \neq 0.$$

Thus if P_i is equivalent to P_j and if P_j is equivalent to P_k, then P_i is equivalent to P_k. (One says that equivalence is reflexive, symmetric, and transitive.) We can divide the projections $P_1, \ldots, P_n$ into disjoint classes such that any two projections in the same class are equivalent and no projection in one class is equivalent to any projection in another class.

We first conclude the proof for the case in which there is only one class. For each $i = 1, \ldots, n$ let S_i be a nonzero operator in M for which $P_i S_i P_1 = S_i$. Select any scalar product on the subspace VP_1 and define the scalar product on VP_i such that if $x, y \in VP_i$, then $(x, y) = (xS_i, yS_i)$. Finally, make the subspaces VP_i pairwise orthogonal, and we have defined a scalar product on V (Problem 9). Obviously each P_i is now a perpendicular projection and each S_i is a partial isometry. As in the proof of Theorem 1, $S_i^* \in M$ also for all i. For any $T \in M$, $(P_i T P_j)(S_j S_i^*) = (P_i T P_j)(S_j S_i^* P_i) = cP_i$ for some scalar c and $(S_j S_i^*)(S_j S_i^*)^* = S_j S_i^* S_i S_j^* P_j = dP_j$ for some nonzero scalar d. Hence

$$P_i T P_j = (P_i T P_j)P_j = d^{-1}(P_i T P_j)(S_j S_i^*)(S_j S_i^*)^*$$
$$= d^{-1}cP_i(S_i S_j^*) = d^{-1}c(S_i S_j^*).$$

Thus every operator in M is a linear combination of operators of the form $S_i S_j^*$. But the adjoint of an operator of this form is again of this form. Hence M is self-adjoint if there is only one class.

When there is more than one class we define in the way just described a scalar product on the sum of the ranges of the projections in each equivalence class, and then make these sums pairwise orthogonal.

Problems for Lecture 5—4

1. In the proof of Theorem 1 explain why if S is a scalar multiple of a partial isometry R, then S_1 is a scalar multiple of R^*.
2. In the proof of Theorem 1 show in detail that the commutant of the contraction of $P_i M$ to $U_i = VP_i$ is the contraction of $P_i M' P_i$ to U_i.
3. In the proof of Theorem 1 explain why the set of all vectors of the form $z + zS$ constitute a subspace of $U_i \oplus U_j$.
4. In the proof of Theorem 1 explain why dim $W = $ dim U_i.
5. In the proof of Theorem 3 show that the stated perpendicular projections P_i exist in M and that $P_i T$ is a scalar multiple of P_i for any $T \in M$.
6. In the proof of Theorem 3 explain why $Q \in M' - M$.
7. In the proof of Theorem 4 show that the desired projections P_i exist.
8. In the proof of Theorem 4 show that an operator S_1 exists in M such that $P_j S_1 P_i = S_1$.
9. In the proof of Theorem 4 show that we have actually defined a scalar product on V.
10. In the proof of Theorem 4 show that the P_i are perpendicular projections and the S_i are partial isometries under the scalar product we constructed.
11. Let T be a diagonable operator on a complex vector space V. Prove that a scalar product can be defined on V so that T is normal on the resulting unitary space.
12. Prove that if M is an operator algebra on a unitary space, then M^* is also an operator algebra.

$\mathcal{L}$ecture 5–5

Operators in Self-Adjoint Operator Algebras. Throughout the present lecture M will denote a self-adjoint operator algebra on a unitary space V. We saw in Lecture 5-4 that $M = M''$, and in particular $1 \in M$. Thus any polynomial in any operator in M is also in M. Note that if T is an operator commuting with every operator in M', then $T \in M$. Our first result shows that M is in fact the smallest self-adjoint operator algebra that contains all the unitary operators or perpendicular projections in M.

Theorem 1. *Let M be a self-adjoint operator algebra on a unitary space V. Then*
(1) *every operator $T \in M$ is a linear combination of unitary operators in M,*
(2) *every operator $T \in M$ is a linear combination of perpendicular projections in M.*

PROOF. Select a nonzero $T \in M$. Since T is a linear combination of the self-adjoint operators $T + T^*$ and $i(T - T^*)$ in M it suffices to assume that T is self-adjoint. Since T is a scalar multiple of $\|T\|^{-1}T$ it suffices to assume that $\|T\| \leq 1$. Then $(z(1 - T^2),z) = (z, z) - (zT^2, z) = (z, z) - (zT, zT) \geq 0$ and $1 - T^2$ is nonnegative. But $(1 - T^2)^{\frac{1}{2}}$ equals a polynomial in $1 - T^2$ and $(1 - T^2)^{\frac{1}{2}} \in M$. Setting $U = T + i(1 - T^2)^{\frac{1}{2}}$ we have $U \in M$ and

$$UU^* = [T + i(1 - T^2)^{\frac{1}{2}}][T - i(1 - T^2)^{\frac{1}{2}}]$$
$$= T^2 + (1 - T^2) = 1$$

since T commutes with $1 - T^2$ and $(1 - T^2)^{\frac{1}{2}}$, and U is a unitary operator in M. But $2T = U + U^*$ and (1) is proved.

To prove (2) let T be a self-adjoint operator in M and note (Lecture 5-3) that T is a linear combination of perpendicular projections each of which equals some polynomial in T.

Next we show that if $T \in M$ then the partial isometry and the nonnegative operator given by the polar decomposition of T are both in M.

Theorem 2. *Let M be a self-adjoint operator algebra on a unitary space V and let T be an operator in M with null space N and polar decomposition $(TT^*)^{\frac{1}{2}}U$. Then $(TT^*)^{\frac{1}{2}}$ and U lie in M, and so do the perpendicular projections with respective ranges VT and N.*

PROOF. Since $(TT^*)^{\frac{1}{2}}$ equals a polynomial in TT^* it is clear that $(TT^*)^{\frac{1}{2}} \in M$. Now let S be any operator in M'. Then $ST = S(TT^*)^{\frac{1}{2}}U = TS = (TT^*)^{\frac{1}{2}}US = (TT^*)^{\frac{1}{2}}SU$ and the operators US and SU coincide on $V(TT^*)^{\frac{1}{2}} = N^{\perp}$. But N must be invariant under S because S commutes with T and consequently $N(SU) = N(US) = (0)$. Finally US and SU coincide on V and $U \in M'' = M$.

The perpendicular projection with range N is $1 - UU^*$ and the perpendicular projection with range VT is U^*U. Both lie in M because $U \in M$, and the proof is complete.

For perpendicular projections P and Q we let $P \vee Q$ denote the perpendicular projection with range $VP + VQ$ and let $P \wedge Q$ denote the perpendicular projection with range $(VP) \cap (VQ)$. We leave it to the reader to show that that if R is a perpendicular projection such that $R \leq P$, $R \leq Q$, then $R \leq P \wedge Q$. If R is a perpendicular projection such that $P \leq R$, $Q \leq R$, then $P \vee Q \leq R$. We have

Theorem 3. *Let P, Q be perpendicular projections in M. Then $P \vee Q \in M$ and $P \wedge Q \in M$.*

PROOF. Let R be a perpendicular projection in M'. Then VP and VQ are invariant under R, and hence so are $V(P \wedge Q)$, $V(P \vee Q)$, $[V(P \wedge Q)]^{\perp}$ and $[V(P \vee Q)]^{\perp}$. Therefore $P \vee Q$ and $P \wedge Q$ commute with R (since their ranges and null spaces are invariant under R) and it follows from Theorem 1 that $P \vee Q \in M'' = M$ and $P \wedge Q \in M'' = M$.

The operator algebra $M \cap M'$ is called the *center* of the operator algebra M. Note that M and M' have the same center. We call M a *factor* if the center of M consists of only the scalar operators. For example, the algebra of all operators on V is a factor. The center of M is obviously commutative.

If M is an operator algebra and if X is a set of vectors, we henceforth let XM denote the span of all the vectors $xT(x \in X, T \in M)$. Clearly XM is an M-invariant subspace of V.

Theorem 4. *Let M be a self-adjoint operator algebra on a unitary space V and let X be a set of vectors in V. Then*

(1) *the perpendicular projection P with range XM is in M',*

(2) *if X is the range of a perpendicular projection in M, then $P \in M \cap M'$.*

PROOF. To prove (1) we observe that XM is M-invariant and so is $(XM)^{\perp}$. Consequently $P \in M'$.

To prove (2) assume that there is a perpendicular projection $Q \in M$ such that $VQ = X$. We must prove that $P \in M$. A simple dimension argument (Problem 1) shows that there is a maximal perpendicular projection $R \in M$ for which $Q \leq R$ and $VR \subset XM$. For any $T \in M$ we claim that $QT(1 - R) = 0$; for otherwise $VQT(1 - R)$ is a subspace of $(XM) \cap [V(1 - R)]$, and by Theorem 2 the perpendicular projection R_1 with range $VQT(1 - R)$ is in M. Hence $R + R_1 \in M$ is a perpendicular projection, which contradicts the maximality of R. This proves that $VQM(1 - R) = (0)$, and it follows that $XM = XMR + XM(1 - R) = XMR \subset VR$ and $XM = VR$. Then $P = R$ and the proof is complete.

For perpendicular projections $P, Q \in M$ we say that P is M-equivalent to Q (written $P \sim Q$) if there exists a partial isometry $U \in M$ such that $UU^* = P$ and $U^*U = Q$. For example, if $T \in M$ then the perpendicular projections P and Q with respective ranges VT and VT^* satisfy $P \sim Q$; U is then the partial isometry in the polar decomposition of T. We write $P \prec Q$ if there exists a partial isometry $U \in M$ with $UU^* = P$, $U^*U \le Q$. If $P \prec Q$ and $Q \prec P$ we easily see that dim $(VP) = $ dim (VQ) and $P \sim Q$. If $P \prec Q$ and $Q \prec R$, then $P \prec R$. To see this suppose $U_1, U_2 \in M$ such that $U_1 U_1^* = P$, $U_1^*U_1 \le Q$, $U_2 U_2^* = Q$, $U_2^*U_2 \le R$; then $(U_1 U_2)(U_1 U_2)^* = U_1 U_2 U_2^* U_1^* = U_1 Q U_1^* = U_1 U_1^* = P$ and $(U_1 U_2)^*(U_1 U_2) = U_2^* U_1^* U_1 U_2 = R(U_2^* U_1^* U_1 U_2)R \le R$. Furthermore, we see that $P \sim P$ for any perpendicular projection P in M. If $P \sim Q$, then $Q \sim P$. If $P \sim Q$ and $Q \sim R$, then $P \sim R$.

Theorem 5. Let $P, Q \in M$ be perpendicular projections. Then there is a perpendicular projection $R \in M \cap M'$ such that $QR \prec PR$ and $P(1 - R) \prec Q(1 - R)$.

PROOF. By a simple dimension argument there is a maximal perpendicular projection $P_1 \in M$ satisfying $P_1 \le P$, $P_1 \prec Q$. There is a perpendicular projection $Q_1 \in M$ satisfying $Q_1 \le Q$ and $P_1 \sim Q_1$. (Why? Problem 2.) Let R be the perpendicular projection with range $V(P - P_1)M$. By Theorem 4 we have $R \in M \cap M'$.

We claim that $[V(P - P_1)M] \subset V[1 - (Q - Q_1)]$. For if $T \in M$ and $(P - P_1)T(Q - Q_1) \ne 0$, the partial isometry U_1 in the polar decomposition of $(P - P_1)T(Q - Q_1)$ lies in M and $U_1 U_1^* \le P - P_1$, $U_1^*U_1 \le Q - Q_1$ and $U_1 U_1^* + P_1 \prec Q$ (Problem 3) contrary to the maximality of P_1. Thus $R \perp (Q - Q_1)$.

Let U be a partial isometry in M for which $UU^* = P_1$, $U^*U = Q_1$. Then $(UR)(UR)^* = URR^*U^* = URU^* = UU^*R = P_1 R$, $(UR)^*(UR) = R^*U^*UR = R^*RU^*U = Q_1 R$, UR is a partial isometry in M and $P_1 R \sim Q_1 R$. But $QR = Q_1 R + (Q - Q_1)R = Q_1 R$ and $QR \prec PR$.

Similarly

$$[U(1 - R)][U(1 - R)]^* = U(1 - R)U^* = UU^*(1 - R)$$
$$= P_1(1 - R),$$
$$[U(1 - R)]^*[U(1 - R)] = (1 - R)U^*U(1 - R)$$
$$= Q_1(1 - R),$$

$U(1 - R)$ is a partial isometry in M and $P_1(1 - R) \sim Q_1(1 - R)$. But $P(1 - R) = P_1(1 - R) + (P - P_1)(1 - R) = P_1(1 - R)$. Hence $P(1 - R) \prec Q(1 - R)$.

This leads directly to a necessary and sufficient condition that M be a factor.

Theorem 6.   *The self-adjoint operator algebra M is a factor iff for any perpendicular projections P, $Q \in M$ either $P \prec Q$ or $Q \prec P$.*

PROOF.   Assume that M is a factor. For perpendicular projections P, $Q \in M$ there exists a perpendicular projection $R \in M \cap M'$ such that $QR \prec PR$ and $P(1 - R) \prec Q(1 - R)$. Since M is a factor, $R = 0$ or $R = 1$, and either $Q \prec P$ or $P \prec Q$.

Now assume M is not a factor. By Theorem 1 there must exist a perpendicular projection $R \in M \cap M'$ such that $R \neq 0$ and $R \neq 1$. If U is a partial isometry in M such that $UU^* = R$, then $U = (UU^*)U = RU = UR$, $U^*U = (UR)^*(UR) = RU^*UR$, and $U^*U(1 - R) = (RU^*UR)(1 - R) = 0$. Thus it is not possible that $R \prec 1 - R$. Similarly it is not possible that $1 - R \prec R$.

Theorem 7.   *If X is a subset of V, then $XMM' = XM'M = X(M \cap M')'$.*

PROOF.   That $XMM' = XM'M$ follows from $MM' = M'M$. Since $MM' \subset (M \cap M')'$ we have also $XMM' \subset X(M \cap M')'$. Now let P be the perpendicular projection with range $XMM' = XM'M$. By Theorem 4, $P \in M \cap M'$. Thus $X(M \cap M')' = (XP)(M \cap M')' = X(M \cap M')'P$ and consequently $X(M \cap M')' \subset VP = XMM'$ and the proof is complete.

Theorem 8.   *Let $T \in M$, let $y = xT$, and let P, Q, $R \in M$ be the perpendicular projections with respective ranges VT^*, yM', and xM'. Then*

(1) $Q \prec R$,

(2)   *if $xP = x$, then $Q \sim R$.*

PROOF.   One immediately obtains $yM' = xTM' = xM'T = VRT$. We have observed that $Q \sim Q_1$ where $Q_1 \in M$ is the perpendicular projection with range $V(RT)^* = V(T^*R)$. Hence $Q \prec R$ and (1) is proved.

If $xP = x$ then $xM' = xPM' = xM'P \subset VP = VT^*$ and $VR = xM'R \subset VT^*R \subset VR$ and $VT^*R = VR$. It follows that $Q \sim R$ and (2) is proved.

Theorem 9.   *Let x_1, $x \in V$, let P_1, P, Q_1, Q denote the perpendicular projections with respective ranges x_1M, xM, x_1M', and xM'. Then $Q_1 \prec Q$ iff there exists a partial isometry $U \in M'$ such that $UU^* = P_1$ and $U^*U \leq P$.*

PROOF.   Assume that there exists a partial isometry $U \in M'$ such that $UU^* = P_1$ and $U^*U \leq P$. Then there is a $y \in xM$ such that $yU^* = x_1$. And there is a $T \in M$ such that $xT = y$. By Theorem 8, $R \prec Q$ where $R \in M$ is the perpendicular projection with range yM'. Then $x_1M' = yU^*M' \subset yM'$ and $Q_1 \leq R$, $Q_1 \prec Q$. The converse is proved by interchanging the roles of M and M'.

Theorem 10.   *Let x_1, x, P_1, Q_1, P, and Q be as in Theorem 9. Then Q_1 is M-equivalent to Q iff P_1 is M'-equivalent to P.*

This follows immediately from Theorem 9.

Theorem 11. *Let X be a subset of V. Then $V = XM$ iff there exists no nonzero $T \in M'$ satisfying $XT = (0)$. Likewise $V = XM'$ iff there exists no nonzero $T \in M$ satisfying $XT = (0)$.*

PROOF. Assume $V = XM$. Then if $T \in M'$ and $XT = (0)$ we have $VT = (XM)T = (XT)M = (0)$ and $T = 0$. Now assume there is no nonzero $T \in M'$ satisfying $XT = (0)$ and let P be the perpendicular projection with range XM. Then we have $XM(1 - P) = XMP(1 - P) = (0)$, $1 - P \in M'$, $1 - P = 0$ and $V = VP = XM$. The rest of the proof can be obtained by interchanging the roles of M and M'.

Theorem 12. *Suppose $x, y \in V$ such that $V = yM$ and there exists no nonzero $T \in M$ with $xT = 0$. Then $V = xM$ and there exists no nonzero $T \in M$ with $yT = 0$.*

PROOF. Let $P \in M'$ be the perpendicular projection with range xM. Then $PP^* = P$, $P^*P \leq 1$, and 1 is the perpendicular projection with range yM. By Theorem 9 there exists a partial isometry $U \in M$ with $UU^* = 1$, the perpendicular projection with range xM', and $U^*U \leq$ the perpendicular projection with range yM'. Then dim $(yM') =$ dim V and $yM' = V$. By Theorem 11 there exists no nonzero $T \in M$ with $yT = 0$. To prove $V = xM$ reverse the roles of M and M' and use Theorem 11 again.

Problems for Lecture 5—5

1. Use a dimension argument to show that in the proof of Theorem 4 there exists a maximal perpendicular projection $R \in M$ for which $Q \leq R$ and $VR \subset XM$.

2. In the proof of Theorem 5 explain why there exists a perpendicular projection $Q_1 \in M$ such that $Q_1 \leq Q$ and $P_1 \sim Q_1$.

3. In the proof of Theorem 5 explain why $U_1U_1{}^* + P_1 \prec Q$.

4. If P, Q, R are perpendicular projections with $P \leq R$, $Q \leq R$, show that $P \vee Q \leq R$. If $R \leq P$, $R \leq Q$ show that $R \leq P \wedge Q$.

5. If M is a self-adjoint operator algebra containing perpendicular projections P and Q, and if $P \prec Q$, $Q \prec P$, show in detail why $P \sim Q$.

6. Complete the proof of Theorem 12 by showing that $V = xM$.

$\mathcal{L}$ecture 5–6

Linear Forms on Self-Adjoint Operator Algebras. Throughout this lecture M will be a self-adjoint operator algebra on a unitary space V. By a *linear form* on M we mean a scalar valued mapping f on M for which $f(aS + bT) = af(S) + bf(T)$ for all scalars a, b and all $S, T \in M$. We say that the linear form f on M is *positive* if $f(T) \geq 0$ for every nonnegative $T \in M$. An example of a linear form on M is found by selecting vectors $x_1, \ldots, x_n, y_1, \ldots, y_n \in V$ and setting $f(T) = \sum_{i=1}^n (x_i T, y_i)$. An example of a positive linear form is given by $f(T) = \sum_{i=1}^n (x_i T, x_i)$. One of our purposes is to show that any linear form (positive linear form) on M can be described in this way.

If f is a positive linear form on M then $f(T)$ is real for any self-adjoint $T \in M$, because T is the difference of two nonnegative operators $\frac{1}{2}(\|T\| + T)$ and $\frac{1}{2}(\|T\| - T)$ in M (Problem 1). If T is any operator in M, self-adjoint or not, then $f(T) + f(T^*) = f(T + T^*)$ and $if(T) - if(T^*) = f(iT - iT^*)$ are real and it follows that $f(T^*) = \overline{f(T)}$. If $S, T \in M$ with $f(TT^*) \neq 0$ we have

$$
\begin{aligned}
0 &\leq f[(S + cT)(S + cT)^*] \\
&= f(SS^* + cTS^* + \bar{c}ST^* + |c|^2 TT^*) \\
&= f(SS^*) + cf(TS^*) + \bar{c}f(ST^*) + |c|^2 f(TT^*)
\end{aligned}
$$

for any scalar c. Setting $c = -f(ST^*)f(TT^*)^{-1}$ we have

$$0 \leq f(SS^*) - 2|f(ST^*)|^2 f(TT^*)^{-1} + |f(ST^*)|^2 f(TT^*)^{-1}$$

and

$$|f(ST^*)|^2 \leq f(SS^*)f(TT^*).$$

The last inequality holds also if $f(SS^*) \neq 0$ and $f(TT^*) = 0$. Indeed $|f(ST^*)|^2 \leq f(SS^*)f(TT^*)$ for all $S, T \in M$; for if $f(SS^*) = f(TT^*) = 0$, then

$$
\begin{aligned}
0 &\leq f[(S + T)(S + T)^*] = f(ST^*) + f(TS^*), \\
0 &\leq f[(S - T)(S - T)^*] = -f(ST^*) - f(TS^*), \\
0 &\leq f[(S + iT)(S + iT)^*] = -if(ST^*) + if(TS^*), \\
0 &\leq f[(S - iT)(S - iT)^*] = if(ST^*) - if(TS^*),
\end{aligned}
$$

158

and it follows that $2f(ST^*) = [f(ST^*) + f(TS^*)] + [f(ST^*) - f(TS^*)] = 0$. Also $|f(TS^*)|^2 \leq f(SS^*)f(TT^*)$.

Lemma 1. *Let M be a self-adjoint operator algebra on a unitary space V and let $x \in V$ such that there is no nonzero $T \in M$ satisfying $xT = 0$. Let f be a linear form on M. Then there exists a vector $y \in xM$ such that $f(T) = (xT, y)$ for all $T \in M$.*

PROOF. We define the mapping g of the unitary space xM into the scalars as follows: $g(xT) = f(T)$ for $T \in M$. Then g is well-defined; for if $xT_1 = xT_2$ then $x(T_1 - T_2) = 0$ and $T_1 - T_2 = 0$. The reader can easily show that g is a linear form on xM. By Lemma 4 of Lecture 5-1 there exists a vector $y \in xM$ such that $g(xT) = (xT, y)$ for all $T \in M$. Then $f(T) = (xT, y)$ for all $T \in M$.

Lemma 2. *Let f be a positive linear form on the self-adjoint operator algebra M and suppose $x \in V$ such that $f(T) \leq (xT, x)$ for all nonnegative $T \in M$. Then there exists an operator $T' \in M'$ such that $f(T) = (xT'T, xT')$ for all $T \in M$.*

PROOF. For $S \in M$, let g be the scalar valued mapping on xM defined $g(xT) = f(TS^*)$ for all $T \in M$. Then g is well-defined; if $xT_1 = xT_2$, $T_1, T_2 \in M$, then

$$|f[(T_1 - T_2)S^*]|^2 \leq f[(T_1 - T_2)(T_1 - T_2)^*]f(SS^*)$$
$$\leq (x(T_1 - T_2), x(T_1 - T_2))(xS, xS) = 0$$

and $f(T_1S^*) = f(T_2S^*)$. The reader can easily show that g is a linear form on xM (Problem 2). By Lemma 4 of Lecture 5-1 there exists a $y \in xM$ such that $g(xT) = (xT, y)$ for all $T \in M$. We define the mapping T_0 of xM into xM by making $(xS)T_0 = y$. Also T_0 is well-defined because if $xS_1 = xS_2$, $S_1, S_2 \in M$, then

$$|f[T(S_1 - S_2)^*]|^2 \leq (xT, xT)(x(S_1 - S_2), x(S_1 - S_2)) = 0$$

and $f(TS_1^*) = f(TS_2^*)$ for all $T \in M$. The reader can easily show that T_0 is an operator on xM (Problem 3). Extend T_0 to an operator on V by making $zT_0 = 0$ for all $z \perp xM$. We have $f(TS^*) = (xT, xST_0)$ for all $S, T \in M$.

Clearly T_0 is nonnegative, because $(xT, xTT_0) = f(TT^*) \geq 0$ for all $T \in M$, and consequently $(zT_0, z) \geq 0$ for all $z \in V$. For $R, S, T \in M$ we have

$$(xR, xSTT_0) = f[R(ST)^*] = f[(RT^*)S^*]$$
$$= (xRT^*, xST_0) = (xR, xST_0T)$$

and (since T_0T and TT_0 map xM into xM) T_0T coincides with TT_0 on xM. If $z \perp xM$ then $zTT_0 = zT_0T = 0$, and we see finally that $T_0 \in M'$.

Set $T' = T_0^{\frac{1}{2}}$. Then $T' \in M'$ and for all $T \in M$, $f(T) = f(T1) = (xT, xT_0) = (xTT', xT') = (xT'T, xT')$. The proof is complete.

We are now ready to prove the major result of our lecture.

Theorem 1.   *Let M be a self-adjoint operator algebra on a unitary space V of dimension n and let f be a linear form on M. Then*

(1)   *there exist vectors $x_1, \ldots, x_n, y_1, \ldots, y_n \in V$ such that $f(T) = \sum_{i=1}^{n} (x_i T, y_i)$ for all $T \in M$.*

(2)   *If f is positive, there exist vectors $z_1, \ldots, z_n$ such that $f(T) = \sum_{i=1}^{n} (z_i T, z_i)$ for all $T \in M$.*

PROOF.   Let $\{x_1, \ldots, x_n\}$ be a basis of V. We define a unitary space V' as follows. The elements of V' are ordered n-tuples $\{z_1, \ldots, z_n\}$ of vectors in V. Addition and scalar multiplication are defined componentwise,

$$a\{z_1, \ldots, z_n\} + b\{w_1, \ldots, w_n\} = \{az_1 + bw_1, \ldots, az_n + bw_n\},$$

and the scalar product is given by $(\{z_1, \ldots, z_n\}, \{w_1, \ldots, w_n\}) = \sum_{i=1}^{n} (z_i, w_i)$. The reader can show that V', with this scalar product, is a unitary space (Problem 4). For each $T \in M$ define the mapping T' of V' into V' as follows: $\{z_1, \ldots, z_n\}T' = \{z_1 T, \ldots, z_n T\}$. One can easily see (Problem 5) that T' is an operator on V', and the set of operators $\{T': T \in M\}$ constitutes a self-adjoint operator algebra on V'. Note that the adjoint of T' is $T^{*'}$.

Putting $f'(T') = f(T)$ we see that f' is a linear form on this operator algebra (Problem 6). Furthermore if $\{x_1, \ldots, x_n\}T' = \{0, \ldots, 0\}$ then $x_i T = 0$ for $i = 1, \ldots, n$ and clearly $T = 0$ on V and $T' = 0$ on V'. By Lemma 1 there is a vector $\{y_1, \ldots, y_n\} \in V'$ such that

$$f(T) = f'(T') = (\{x_1, \ldots, x_n\}T', \{y_1, \ldots, y_n\}) = \sum_{i=1}^{n} (x_i T, y_i)$$

for all $T \in M$. Thus (1) is proved.

It can be shown easily (Problem 7) that T' is nonnegative iff T is nonnegative. Assume that f is positive; it follows that f' is also positive. For T' nonnegative we have

$$0 \leq f'(T') = \sum_i (x_i T, y_i) = \sum_i \overline{(x_i T, y_i)}$$
$$= \sum_i \overline{(x_i, y_i T)} = \sum_i (y_i T, x_i)$$

and consequently

$$4f'(T') = \sum_i ((x_i + y_i) T, (x_i + y_i)) - \sum_i ((x_i - y_i) T, (x_i - y_i))$$
$$\leq \sum_i ((x_i + y_i) T, (x_i + y_i))$$

and

$$f'(T') \leq (\{\tfrac{1}{2}(x_1 + y_1), \ldots, \tfrac{1}{2}(x_n + y_n)\}T',$$
$$\{\tfrac{1}{2}(x_1 + y_1), \ldots, \tfrac{1}{2}(x_n + y_n)\}).$$

By Lemma 2 there is a vector $\{z_1, \ldots, z_n\} \in V'$ such that $f'(T') = (\{z_1, \ldots, z_n\}T', \{z_1, \ldots, z_n\})$ for all $T \in M$. This proves (2).

Lemma 3. *Let f be a linear form on a self-adjoint operator algebra M on a unitary space V. Then the following are equivalent.*
(1) $f(ST) = f(TS)$ *for all* $S, T \in M$.
(2) $f(UTU^{-1}) = f(T)$ *for all nonnegative operators* $T \in M$ *and all unitary operators* $U \in M$.

PROOF. Assume (1). Then if T is a nonnegative operator in M and if U is a unitary operator in M we have $f(UTU^{-1}) = f(TU^{-1}U) = f(T)$.

Now assume (2). If T_1, T_2, T_3, T_4 are nonnegative operators in M and if U is unitary then

$$f[U(T_1 - T_2 + iT_3 - iT_4)U^{-1}]$$
$$= f(UT_1U^{-1}) - f(UT_2U^{-1}) + if(UT_3U^{-1}) - if(UT_4U^{-1})$$
$$= f(T_1) - f(T_2) + if(T_3) - if(T_4) = f(T_1 - T_2 + iT_3 - iT_4).$$

It follows that for $T \in M, f(UTU^{-1}) = f(T)$, and $f(U(TU)U^{-1}) = f(TU) = f(UT)$. Since any $S \in M$ is a linear combination of unitary operators in M we have $f(ST) = f(TS)$ for all $S, T \in M$.

Theorem 2. *Let V be a unitary space of dimension n, and let $\{z_1, \ldots, z_n\}$ be an orthonormal basis of V. Let f be the linear form on the algebra M of all operators on V given by $f(T) = \sum_{i=1}^{n}(z_iT, z_i)$. Then*
(1) $f(1) = n$.
(2) $f(UTU^{-1}) = f(T)$ *for all nonnegative $T \in M$ and all unitary $U \in M$.*
Furthermore if g is a linear form on M satisfying (1) and (2), then $g = f$.

PROOF. Clearly $f(1) = \sum_{i=1}^{n}(z_i, z_i) = n$ and this proves (1). To prove (2) we have

$$f(T) = \sum_{i=1}^{n}(z_iT, z_i) = \sum_{i=1}^{n}\|z_iT^{\frac{1}{2}}\|^2$$
$$= \sum_i \sum_j |(z_iT^{\frac{1}{2}}, z_jU)|^2 = \sum_j \sum_i |(z_jUT^{\frac{1}{2}}, z_i)|^2$$
$$= \sum_j \|z_jUT^{\frac{1}{2}}\|^2 = \sum_j (z_jUT, z_jU)$$
$$= \sum_j (z_jUTU^{-1}, z_j) = f(UTU^{-1}).$$

Now suppose g is a linear form on M satisfying (1) and (2). Let P be a perpendicular projection whose range has dimension 1. We can easily find unitary operators $U_1, \ldots, U_n$ such that $U_iPU_i^{-1}$ is the perpendicular projection whose range is the 1-dimensional subspace spanned by z_i. Then $n = g(1) = \sum_{i=1}^{n} g(U_iPU_i^{-1}) = ng(P)$ because $g(P) = g(U_iPU_i^{-1})$ for all i. Hence $g(P) = 1$ and the same argument on f shows that $f(P) = 1$. Inasmuch as any perpendicular projection $Q \in M$ is the sum of perpendicular projections in M whose ranges have dimension 1 we have $f(Q) = g(Q)$. Since any operator in M is a linear combination of perpendicular projections in M we have $f = g$ on M.

Note that f was independent of the choice of orthonormal basis $\{z_1, \ldots, z_n\}$. For if g were the linear form thus obtained from another orthonormal basis, g would satisfy (1) and (2) and we would have $f = g$. This linear form f is sometimes called the *trace* on the algebra of all operators on V. Indeed we can define the trace for operators on an arbitrary complex vector space V of dimension n (not necessarily unitary) to be the linear form on the algebra of all operators satisfying $f(1) = n$, $f(ST) = f(TS)$ for all S and T. By assigning a scalar product to V, we see from Lemma 3 and Theorem 2 that one and only one such linear form f exists (Problem 8).

Problems for Lecture 5—6

1. Show that for any operator T on a unitary space, the operators $\|T\| + T$ and $\|T\| - T$ are nonnegative.
2. In the proof of Lemma 2 show that g is a linear form on xM.
3. In the proof of Lemma 2 show that T_0 is an operator on xM.
4. In the proof of Theorem 1 show that V' with the scalar product we constructed is a unitary space.
5. Show that the T' referred to in the proof of Theorem 1 is an operator on V', and show that the set of operators $\{T': T \in M\}$ constitutes a self-adjoint algebra of operators on V'. Show that the adjoint of T' on V' is $T^{*\prime}$.
6. In the proof of Theorem 1 show that f' is a linear form on the operator algebra considered.
7. In the proof of Theorem 1 show that T is nonnegative on V iff T' is nonnegative on V'.
8. Show that there is a unique linear form f on a complex n-dimensional vector space satisfying $f(1) = n$ and $f(ST) = f(TS)$ for all S and T.
9. Show that the trace of any projection P on a complex vector space equals dim VP.
10. Use Problem 9 to prove the following statement: if $P_1, \ldots, P_k$ are projections on a complex vector space V and if $\sum_i P_i$ is also a projection, then the P_i are pairwise orthogonal. (Hint: set $P_{k+1} = 1 - \sum_{i=1}^{k} P_i$, show that the subspaces VP_i are linearly independent, join together bases of the VP_i to form a basis of V and consider matrices of the P_i.)
11. In Problem 8 show that $f(T)$ equals the sum of the elements on the main diagonal of any matrix associated with T.

Bibliography

1. S. K. Berberian, "Introduction to Hilbert Space," 1961, Oxford University Press.
2. T. Botts and E. J. McShane, "Real Analysis," 1959, D. van Nostrand.
3. C. W. Curtis, "Linear Algebra," 1963, Allyn & Bacon.
4. J. Dixmier, "Les Algèbres d'Opérateurs dans L'espace Hilbertiens," 1957, Gauthier-Villars.
5. P. R. Halmos, "Naive Set Theory," 1960, D. van Nostrand.
6. P. R. Halmos, "Finite Dimensional Vector Spaces," 1958, D. van Nostrand.
7. Nathan Jacobson, "Abstract Algebra," vol. II, 1953, D. van Nostrand.
8. Nathan Jacobson, "Structure of Rings," 1956, American Mathematical Society.
9. I. Kaplansky, "Infinite Abelian Groups," 1954, The University of Michigan Press.
10. J. L. Kelley, "General Topology," 1955, D. van Nostrand.
11. W. Rudin, "Principles of Mathematical Analysis," 1964, McGraw-Hill.
12. M. F. Smiley, "Algebra of Matrices," 1965, Allyn & Bacon.

Index